A BRIEF HISTORY OF
SCIENCE

DEDICATION

This book is respectfully dedicated to
Students of Science and Philosophy.

Also to the General Reader
to laugh at the absurdities of Mankind,
to weep at the misfortunes of Mankind,
and to rage at the cruelties and injustices of the World;
above all, to think, and to ponder and to
realise the huge gaps in our knowledge and
understanding of the World.

A BRIEF HISTORY OF
SCIENCE

J. W. MALTBY

HALSGROVE

First published in Great Britain in 2003

British Library Cataloguing-in-Publication Data
A CIP record for this title is available from the British Library

ISBN 1 84114 323 5

HALSGROVE

Halsgrove House
Lower Moor Way
Tiverton, Devon EX16 6SS
Tel: 01884 243242
Fax: 01884 243325
email sales@halsgrove.com
website www.halsgrove.com

Printed and bound in Great Britain by
The Cromwell Press, Trowbridge

CONTENTS

LIST OF PLATES

i. Sculpture 'Ex tenebris Lux' at the Robert McDougall Art Gallery in Christchurch New Zealand.

ii Geological Timetable - based upon *Geology* by Frank H.T. Rhodes. Golden Press Western Publishing Company Inc. Racine, Wisconsin.

iii Carl Linnaeus, naturalist, dressed in traditional Saami (Lapp) costume. Engraved by Henry Kingsbury and published in 1805. *The Bridgeman Art Library.*

iv Portrait of Sir Benjamin Thompson, Count Romford, by Thomas Gainsborough. American adventurer, philosopher, philanthropist, philanderer. Joint founder of the Royal Institution. *Fogg Art Museum, Harvard University.*

v. Portrait of Sir Joseph Banks by Sir Joshua Reynolds. Looking relaxed and confident, as well he might, considering the time he had spent in the bed of a Tahitian princess. Later President of the Royal Society. The genus of Australian shrubs *Banksia* is named after him. *The Bridgeman Art Library.*

vi. Portrait of Thomas Henry Huxley by Alphonse Legros. *The Bridgeman Art Library.*

vii. The Periodic Table.

viii. The Electromagnetic Spectrum.

PROLOGUE

Not to know what happened before you were born is to remain a child all your life – Marcus Tullius **Cicero**, Roman Writer, orator and Consul - (106–43BC)

History is bunk – Henry **Ford**, American motorcar manufacturer. (1863–1947) [Especially that purveyed by Hollywood – marketing is all!]

Minds emerge from process and interaction, not from substance – Paul Broks

'Supposing' is good - 'Finding out' is better – **Mark Twain**, *nom de plume* of Samuel Clemens, Mississippi steamboat pilot and American author. (1835–1910)

By doubting one comes to questioning. And by questioning we perceive the truth. – Peter **Abelard**, monk. AD1122. [*but* – Old Hungarian proverb: 'tell the truth and get your head bashed in'.]

All that is essential in Life is unseen.

The supreme achievement of reason is to realise that there is a limit to reason. – Blaise **Pascal**

We could live at the present day without a Plato, but a double number of Newtons is required to discover the secrets of Nature and to bring life into harmony with the laws of Nature. – **Mendeleeff**

How technologically vulnerable the whole of modern civilisation has become. – Acedemician Georgiy Arbatov. *Pravda*, 9 May 1986 [In the wake of the Chernobyl disaster.]

It ain't what I don't know what worries me.
It's what I know as ain't so. – Mark Twain

A BRIEF HISTORY OF SCIENCE

Definitions only survive their utility, like everything else.

Certain systems of thought or paradigms dominate a profession's thinking in such a way that they are passed on unquestioned from one generation to the next. – Michael *Eraut* 1944.

Prior to the eighteenth century it was necessary to Latinize one's name. Latin was the *lingua franca* of science in those days. The Polish priest Nicolaus Koppernigk became **Copernicus**. Miguel **Serveto** from Navarre became Servetus. The map-maker **Mercator** (1512–1594) was born Gerard Kremer: Kremer means merchant in German. A mercator was a travelling bookseller at the time. He used the word 'Atlas' for a collection of maps. The English tended to stick to their original names.

It has to be borne in mind that some of the assertions made in this book will subsequently shown to be misleading or possibly incorrect. Corrections will of course be included in subsequent editions, if any

The Index includes names in **bold** and subjects in ***bold italics***

CHAPTER ONE

WHAT IS SCIENCE?

S cience is based on 0bservation, Measurement, Recording, and the formulation of Theories to account for and to explain the observations, and Experiments to confirm or refute the theories

It is perhaps unfortunate that Science has fallen into disrepute as an intellectual discipline because its existence has too often depended on 'the crumbs that have fallen from the table of a Weapons Development Programme'.

Another definition if science is 'an adventure at the frontier of uncertainty'. That which people seek more than anything is certainty and repose. Yet certainty (except death and taxes of course) is an illusion and repose is for the dead. Paradoxically, it is the uncertainty of the lottery, the horse race or football match that provides great stimulus for activity. It has been estimated that £3 trillion are spent yearly on gambling.

Scientific method is based on logic, premises, inferences and deductions. It assumes that phenomena are causally related and do not happen by chance. Effect A may be caused by B but there may be an intermediate, and as yet unknown cause, C.

Incorrect use of words leads to confusion of thought. Definitions must be as clear as possible. Arcane and priestly language may be satisfactory for the initiated but it is necessary for the rest of us to understand what is going on, what it is all about, and to make an attempt to understand scientific terminology. Clarity and lucidity is the keynote. One must never mistake obscurity for profundity. The *'Fog Index'* is a useful measure of impenetrability. It is calculated by taking a passage of about 100 words and dividing the number of words by the number of sentences. To this is added the percentage of the number of words with 3 or more syllables in the passage of 100 words. This gives the Fog Index – the readability figure. The higher the value, the less readable the text. An index of 23 might be typical for an economics textbook, 12–13 for a *Times* editorial, 8 for a novel. Police are advised to aim for 10–12.

There is now a computer programme called *'Bullfighter'* which detects the meaningless jargon in the speeches of politicians and management consultants (no offence!). Words such as 'empower', 'transparent', 'leverage', 'affordable' and 'global', are detected, together with the length of sentence, and a 'bull index' measured.

Knowledge and imagination are both necessary (Einstein claimed that imagination was more important than knowledge). Yet the greatest imaginative leap in the, at times, lamentable history of *Homo sapiens,* was the association of a visual image with a sound – the origin of writing and reading, which occurred about 10,000 years ago.

'Science does not deal with ultimates, but rather relations between observed and observable phenomena.' (R.A. Milliken).

Science not only attempts to explain 'how', it also attempts to explain 'why'. It was known for centuries that if one constructs a triangle whose sides are 3, 4, and 5 units, the angle opposite the side with 5 units would be a right angle. It took the genius of the Greek mathematician and philosopher **Pythagoras** (580–500BC) to explain why. There is no other word in the English language of comparable length and decency with such force as that word 'why'. It is the ultimate appeal to the Court of Reason.

By inductive reasoning a tentative *hypothesis* may be formed. If, by mathematical or experimental means, there are no discrepancies, the hypothesis becomes a *theory*. Then, with the passage of time, no better equations or attempts to disprove the theory have been found, it becomes a *Law*. 'By a theory I mean a conclusion drawn from the accumulated facts we now possess which enables us to foresee facts which we do not yet know.' (Mendeleeff).

Statistical analysis is used in an attempt to eliminate random effects, to improve confidence in the conclusions.

(Rutherford said that if you have to call in a statistician to evaluate your experiment - design a better experiment).

Observation, and the testing by *experiment*, provides *evidence*, and science, like law, must be based on objective evidence. Experiments must be capable of universal reproduction and observations must be generally agreed.

Measurement consists of laying an unknown against a known. The known must be an Internationally agreed Standard.

In the past physical science was known as Natural Philosophy. *Philosophy* is the search for wisdom and knowledge, for basic causes and ultimate *reality*. Yet what is reality? It has two elements the *objective* (The Primary Qualities of Galileo) – the external world, and the *subjective* (The Secondary Qualities of Galileo), that arise from individual consciousness (the 5 senses - sight, hearing, touch, taste and smell – some assert that there are 6). This distinction is made in medical practice. *Symptoms* are subjective, how the patient feels and what he says. *Signs* are objective, what the doctor finds on examination by observation, hearing (auscultation) and touch (palpation). Further tests such as blood tests or X-rays are also objective. At least this is the classical view. It may well be that objectivity is merely relative – comparing one observation with another. Perhaps reality is other people.

The essence of *discovery* is *description* – how to get there and what you find, what it looks like (properties), when you have got there. Having got there and returned, one then has to convince others. This is not always easy.

Definition of terms is crucial to science so that a common knowledge can be shared. 'Particle' is difficult to define, does it mean that which has mass? Here unfortunately we enter the realm of metaphysics, a concept which is beyond the scope of this book.

CHAPTER TWO

BASICS

A knowledge of mathematics is essential to science, since all measurements are expressed numerically. The idea of numbers is a comparatively recent one in evolutionary time. Some primitive tribes can only count up to three – larger numbers are beyond their comprehension and are called 'many'. The cipher 0 (zero) is a comparatively recent concept, appearing about the eleventh century AD.

The notation we use today is called the decimal system since it is based on units of 10, and the characters are called Arabic numerals (though Arabic numbers today are quite different). It would be more accurate to call them Hindu-Arabic numerals, since there is some evidence that they were first seen in Hindu writing.

Roman numerals – I, II, III, IV(4), V(5), X(10), L(50), C(100), D(500), M(1000), are only used for kings, clocks, and dates at present. There is a recent return to this notation of using letters for numbers – we now have K (Kilo) to mean 1,000, and M (Mega) to mean one million. Perhaps it will not be long before we have Bn – one billion – 1,000,000,000 – 10^9. This is the American billion and is a more useful quantity than the English billion a million million, which is falling into disuse. Then Tr for trillion – 10^{12} (Japanese yen currency), and Qn for quadrillion – 10^{15}. Then Googol for 10^{100}

The decimal system perhaps arose because we have 10 fingers. At any rate, single numbers are called digits, from the Latin for finger.

The binary system, used in computers, is based on a unit of 2. This is because the processors in the computer consist of millions of switches, which are either on (1) or off (0).

The decimal system makes use of dots 'decimal points' instead of fractions. $1/2$ is written 0.5 and $1/4$ as 0.25 etc. A superscript or power or exponent can be used as a multiplication factor to indicate very large or very small numbers. Thus, using the base of 10, 1 is 10^0, 10 is 10^1, 100 is 10^2, 1/10 is 10^{-1}, 1/100 is 10^{-2} etc. These exponents are given names, such as Kilo meaning 10^3 or 1000 times. That is, a Kilogram is 1000 grams.

In general, it is best to avoid decimal points, by bringing the figure to a whole number and adding a multiplier. Thus, instead of writing 0.032% as the concentration of carbon dioxide in the atmosphere, it is best to write 320 parts per million, or possibly 320×10^{-6}.

See Appendix 1 for list of prefixes.

There are three fundamental units to consider, mass, length and time (but see below SI units where there are 7 base units). If the Theory of Relativity is correct these are related thus:

1. Mass. $m = \dfrac{m_0}{\sqrt{(1 - v^2/c^2)}}$

where m_0 is rest mass, m is the mass of a body with a velocity v with respect to an observer, and c is the velocity of light (300,000km per sec).

It will be seen that when v is zero, the body is stationary and $m_0 = m$. When $v = c$, m will be infinite.

It has been proved experimentally with basic particles like electrons.

A distinction has to be made between mass and weight. Weight is mass times the force of gravity. A kilogram mass on Earth would only weigh one-fifth of a kilogram on the Moon as the mass of the Moon is only one fifth of the mass of the Earth, and only exerts one fifth of the gravitational force of the Earth. A body in space, free of a gravitational field, would still have mass but no weight. Astronauts are weightless because the force of the Earth's gravitational field is exactly balanced by the centrifugal (rotational) force due to their orbital velocity, though they still have mass.

Rotation is the condition of stability, as every navigator with his gyro-compass, child with his spinning top, marksman with his rifle, cyclist and figure-skater knows. Everything spins, from electrons, protons, to neutron stars and galaxies. Mathematically, rotation is the reciprocal of time, 1/t. In mechanics a rotating body is said to have angular momentum which, like mass and energy (with the exception of nuclear transformations) must be conserved. Energy is stored by rotating bodies.

There are two critical angular velocities. Too slow, and the top or bicycle falls over. Too fast, and the flywheel disintegrates, as centrifugal force exceeds the cohesive force of its constituent particles.

Left and right, east and west, are consequences of rotation.

Rotation is measured in revolutions per minute (rpm) and frequency (which is also 1/t) in cycles per second, now to be called Hertz.

Other properties of rotation of a rapidly spinning body such as a gyroscope are rigidity of its axis in space, and *precession*. The first is similar to Newton's first law of motion, in that its axis remains constant unless a force acts on it to change it. When such a force is applied, the axis of rotation moves at right angles to the direction of the applied force. This is known as precession.

MEASUREMENT OF WEIGHT

1. Imperial System – (f p s, based on standard units of a foot, a pound and a second.)

Historical note – the late eighteenth century was a time of much social change. In 1790 the French invited the English to join in an International System for Weights and Measures. No action was taken. In 1871 the House of Commons rejected by five votes a Bill to make the metric system compulsory. In 1897 the metric system was legalised. In 1968 the Federation of British Industries proposed metrication, as half British exports went to metric countries. The Government accepted this and a Standing Joint Committee was set up, and the Metrication Board established in an advisory capacity, with its term expiring in 1980.

Schools in the UK adopted the metric System in 1974. The USA was committed to voluntary metrication in 1975, reaffirmed by the Carter administration in 1979, though by 2003 it still hasn't happened. In Australia and Canada miles were replaced by kilometres and metrication was virtually complete by 1980. In South Africa metrication was complete by 1977, and regulations prohibiting the use of Imperial units were introduced. In India and New Zealand metrication was virtually complete by 1979. In 1979 the London Commodity Market went metric. In 1981 the European Economic Community directed the use of SI units to come into effect by the end of 1989. Degrees Fahrenheit, yards and knots etc. must go!

But neither the Government nor the people were keen to see this happen. Thus it has taken over a hundred years for metrication to be established in the UK, where it is still not complete. The USA has rejected attempts at metrication, which has caused problems with science and engineering. But, 200 years after metrication, half a kilo is still *une livre* in French markets. Traditions die hard.

Imperial Weights

a. *Avoirdupois*. This was based on a pound of 7,000 grains. A grain was a grain of wheat, equal to 64.8 milligrams.

The Standard Pound is a cylinder of platinum introduced in 1855, kept in the Standards Office, with copies kept at the Royal Mint, the Royal Observatory and the Royal Society. The pound was divided into 16 ounces, one ounce is equal to 28.35 grams. There are 453.6 grams in a pound avoirdupois.

There are about 2.2 pounds in a kilogram.

There are 14 pounds in a stone, eight stones in a hundredweight, twenty hundredweight in a ton (2,240 pounds). In the US a short hundredweight is 100 pounds and a short ton is 2000 pounds.

b. *Troy*. This was introduced in 1527, probably from France, (the town of Troyes). It was based on a pound of 5,760 grains.

There are 12 ounces in a Troy pound, one ounce being equal to 31.1 grams. Gold is still traded in Troy ounces, and in $US, though Troy units are no longer legal in the UK.

c. Precious stones are traded in *carats*, one carat is $3^1/_{16}$ grains, 205.5 milligrams. The origin of this may be from the weight of a carob seed. Another meaning of carat is the purity of gold, 24 carat is 100% gold.

Metric weights (from the Greek metros, a measure).
The unit of mass is the kilogram, originally defined as the weight of a litre of water at 4° centigrade. The standard now is a platinum/iridium cylinder kept at Sèvres in France. A copy, No.20, is kept at the US National Institute of Standards and Technology.
   A *gram* is a one-thousandth part of a kilogram. A metric tonne is a thousand kilograms, 2,200 pounds avoirdupois.

MEASUREMENT OF LENGTH
In the ancient world the unit of length was the *stade* – the distance Hercules could run without taking a breath. It was about 605 feet, 201 yards, or 184 metres. The race was called a stade, and the place where it took place in Olympia, a stadium.
   The Biblical cubit was the distance between the elbow and the tip of the middle finger, about 43 centimetres (anatomically the *cubital fossa* is at the bend of the elbow). Noah's Ark (*Genesis* Chapter 6) was 300 cubits long, about 130 metres, 426 feet.
   Today we have $l_0 = l \sqrt{(1 - v^2/c^2)}$, where l is the length of a rod moving with a velocity v with respect to an observer, l_0 is its length at rest and c is the velocity of light. This is known as the Lorenz–Fitzgerald transformation, or contraction. It is a consequence of the measuring rod contracting equally with the rod to be measured, only of significance at velocities approaching that of light.

Imperial System
The base unit the *yard*, used as a standard for 800 years, was the length of the arm of King Henry I (1100–1135) from nose to fin-

ger tip. Hence the 'Imperial' system. The yard is divided into three feet, a foot is divided into three hands (used only for measuring horses now.) A foot is also divided into 12 inches. The Standard Yard is the distance between two marks on a bronze bar at 62°F kept at the National Physical Laboratory.

The standard inch is now defined as 2.54 centimetres – correct to one part in a million. There are 36 inches in a yard, and 39.37 inches in a metre. There are 1760 yards in a statute mile, or 5280 feet. A furlong is an eighth of a mile, 220 yards. It is only used in horse racing today.

Another unit, used in navigation, is the *knot*, or nautical mile. This is equal to one minute of arc of latitude (or longitude at the Equator) of the Earth's circumference. The calculation is as follows: the circumference of the Earth is about 24,000 statute miles. There are 360 degrees in a circle. 24,000 divided by 360 is 66.66 statute miles. This is a degree of latitude or longitude at the equator. There are 60 minutes in a degree: 66.6 divided by 60 gives 1.11, and one minute of arc is a knot. Therefore a knot is 1.11 statute miles. The English nautical mile is equal to 6080 feet. The knot is more commonly used as a unit of speed, being one nautical mile per hour. Other nautical units are the cable (608 or 720 feet), and the fathom (6 feet), which is the depth of water a man could stand in without drowning (he must be pretty tall!).

A kilometre is $^5/_8$ of a mile, there are 62.5 miles to 100 kilometres. There are 160 kilometres to 100 miles.

Other units derived from length are:
1. Unit of <u>area</u> (1^2) is the *acre*, which is defined as 4840 square yards, about 70 yards square. There are 640 acres to the square mile. The acre was originally the space a ploughmen with a horse could plough in a day.
2. <u>Volume</u> (1^3) is based on the standard *gallon*. A gallon is defined as the volume of 10 pounds of water at 62°F. and 30 inches of mercury barometric pressure. There are 8 pints in a gallon and 16 fluid ounces in a pint. There are 28.4 millilitres in a fluid ounce, and 568 millilitres in an Imperial pint. There are 2 pints in a quart – a quarter of a gallon.

The *bushel* is still in use in the USA as a measure of produce and contains 8 US gallons, equal to 30.28 litres, but this varies depending on the commodity.

The *barrel* is a unit of volume. It is still in use for trading petroleum. Its volume depends on the substance concerned. There are 42 US gallons (35 UK gallons) in a barrel, equal to 159 litres, for petrol. For alcohol it is 189 litres. A barrel of flour weighs 196 pounds, of beans 280 pounds.

The US *gallon*, the old Queen Anne Gallon, is 4/5 of the Imperial Gallon, equal to 3,785.4 millilitres compared with 4,456 millilitres in the Imperial Gallon.

As there are 8 pints in a gallon, the US pint (American liquid measure) is smaller than the Imperial pint, being only 473.2 millilitres.

Tonnage of shipping was introduced in order to ascertain the charges to be levied for port or pilotage facilities. It was originally based on a unit of 100 cubic feet but is now based on a unit of 40 cubic feet, the assumption being that that is the volume of 1 ton avoirdupois. At any rate it is a measure of carrying capacity or volume and may well have been derived from the Old English word 'tun'.

Metric System

The base unit of length is the *metre*. This was originally based on a unit that was to be one ten-millionth of the quadrant of the Earth's circumference, of a meridian passing through Paris. In 1790 the National Assembly of France set up a committee to consider these proposals, and a commission was appointed to measure a meridian (line of longitude) between Dunkirk and Mont Jany, near Barcelona. It reported in 1799 and in 1801 a law was passed making the system compulsory, in France at any rate. One of the problems was that some of the measurers, with their white flags, were mistaken for the Aristocracy in Revolutionary France, and were guillotined.

In 1875 the International Bureau of Weights and Measures was established in Paris. Owing to the difficulties inherent in the original definition of the metre, it was superseded in 1899 by the International Prototype Metre which consisted of the distance between marks on a standard bar of 90% platinum and 10% iridium.

The development of the *interferometer* by A. A. **Michelson** while Professor of Physics at the Case School of Applied Science at Cleveland Ohio in the late nineteenth century led to the ability to measure length with great precision using a beam of light (he received the Nobel Prize for physics in 1907). He measured the metre with great accuracy and constancy using cadmium light, and was appointed to the International Conference of Weights and Measures in 1897. This committee meets every six years.

In 1927 the Conference adopted as a provisional standard that a metre was to be 1,553,164.13 wavelengths of the red light emitted by a cadmium vapour lamp under specified conditions. This was accurate to one part in ten million. It has now been superseded – see below.

One thousand metres make one kilometre. One thousandth part is a millimetre and a millionth part is a micron, or μ.

A kilometre is ⁵/₈ of a mile. There are 160 kilometres in 100 miles, and 62.5 miles in 100 kilometres.

The unit of area is the *are*, which is one square metre. A hectare is 100 metres square, or 10,000 square metres. There are 2.4 acres to a hectare, and one acre is 0.405 of a hectare. There are 100 hectare to a square kilometre and 256 hectare to a square mile.

The unit of volume is the *litre*, now defined as the volume of one kilogram of water at 40°C at normal atmospheric pressure. Originally the gramme was defined as the weight of a cubic centimetre of water, and the notation cc is used – but only for motor car engines now. The usual notation now is to use millilitres – ml for one thousandth part of a litre.

There are 28.4 millilitres to a (UK) fluid ounce, about 543 millilitres to an Imperial pint. There are 29.5 millilitres to a US fluid ounce, 473 millilitres to a US pint.

MEASUREMENT OF TIME

Time is the perception of repetition of observations, such as pulse beat, a pendulum swinging, the alternation of day and night, the perception of sequence.

The Sun governs our lives. Any system of time must relate to the apparent motion of the Sun. Solar Day is defined as the interval of time between successive transits of the Sun across the same meridian. It is divided into 24 equal parts – hours – which are again divided into 60 minutes which are again divided into 60 seconds. An observers' instant of the Solar Day is called local time.

The Siderial Day is the interval of time between two successive transits of the first point of Aries across the same meridian (see Astronomy, Chapter 3). It is 23 hours 56 minutes 40 seconds of a mean solar day, owing to the motion of the Earth around the Sun. In practice, the rotational period is marked by observing successive transits of a star across the same meridian.

Greenwich Time is the local time of an observer standing on the meridian of Greenwich – Longitude 0⁰0".

Universal Time is the mean solar time on the meridian of Greenwich. UTo and UT1 are corrections applied due to variations of the Earth's axis of rotation. They do not amount to more than 30 milliseconds.

Coordinated Universal Time or atomic time is based on the natural frequency of oscillation of the caesium atom. The caesium clock was developed by the English physicist Louis Essen in 1955. It was described as the greatest advance in timekeeping since John Harrison's chronometer in the eighteenth century. Essen also developed the quartz crystal clock.

The caesium clock provides a running total of seconds from an arbitrary starting point. It must be coordinated with solar time for time signals. Atomic time has to be kept in step with UT1 by making leap seconds from time to time to ensure that there is no more than 0.7 seconds difference. It has been found necessary to add about 1 leap second a year on average since the atomic clock was started in the 1950s, indicating that the rotation of the Earth is slowing down, probably due to tidal drag. Thus in about 31,563,000 years (the number of seconds in a year – other things being equal, which they seldom are – only one side of the Earth will face the Sun. (Guess who will be lying there on their sunbeds!). After that the Earth will start receding from the Sun, just as the Moon, which is in gravitational lock with the Earth (only one side faces the Earth), is receding from the Earth, a few inches a year.

The **Second** is defined in SI units as the duration of 9,192,631,770 cycles of radiation corresponding to the transition between two hyperfine levels of the ground state of the Caesium-133 atom (1968 – accurate to 1 in 10^{14} and the most exactly known of all the base units).

Historical Note. Primitive man no doubt used a sundial to give an approximate idea of the local time. A burning candle or egg-timer could be used. The Greeks and Romans used a water-clock called a clepsydra (from the Greek *kleptein* – to steal, and *udor* – water) one of whose principal functions was to limit the length of political speeches in the Senate. 'Give him water' – the senators would cry to a particularly good orator.

It was not until the fourteenth century that time measurement became important for purposes of navigation. Portuguese sailors went to sea under the direction of Prince Henry the Navigator (1394–1460). He never actually went to sea, but his mariners used the magnetic compass for navigation, and explored and colonised the Islands of Madeira, Cape Verde, and the Azores. Latitude in the northern hemisphere could be estimated by observing the elevation of the Pole Star above the horizon, and longitude by complex astronomical calculations, '*ephemerides*' involving the position and phases of the Moon, and the positions of the planets – impossible in bad weather. An accurate knowledge of local time was essential for precise determination of longitude, in fog or cloud.

Matters came to a head on 22 October 1707, when the English fleet, returning from an expedition to Spain and France, laden with booty no doubt, became becalmed in fog in the Western Approaches to the English Channel, close by the Bishop Rock. The fleet, including HMS *Association*, HMS *Eagle* and HMS *Romney*, was under the command of Sir Cloudesley Shovell, who summoned his captains to his flagship, HMS *Association*, to discuss their position.

'I knows where we are, Sir' the cabin boy said. 'We are off the Isles of Scilly.'

'How do you know, lad?' said the Admiral.

'I can smell 'em, Sir,' he replied.

The stench of cormorant's nests in the area is well known. but, so the story goes, they took him down and flogged him for insolence with the cat o'nine tails.

The Royal Navy was famous at the time for rum, sodomy and the lash. The penalty for sodomy was death by hanging. This caused a shortage of personnel problem – solved by the introduction of press gangs. In China it was so common in the port of Shanghai - that the word has entered the English language.

Shovell's fleet ran on to the Western Rocks and 800 sailors perished in the disaster (some reports say 2,000), with only 25 survivors, an event comparable to the sinking of the *Titanic* in 1912. The body of the Admiral was washed up at Porthellick Cove, near Hugh Town, the capital of the Isles of Scilly, a few days later, minus his ring finger and 'a fine Emerald Ring'.

The inhabitants of the Isles of Scilly survived in part on shipwrecks that were common at the time, and anything washed ashore was theirs. A woman later confessed to having taken the ring and it was returned to the Admiral's friend, the Earl of Berkeley, but it was subsequently lost.

When news of the disaster reached the Admiralty in London it was decided to set up a Board of Longitude – an early Quango (Quasi-Autonomous Non-Governmental Organisation). In 1998 *Shelgate's Dictionary of Quangos* listed 420, but this was not comprehensive.

A prize of £20,000 equivalent to £800,000 (or US$1,200,000 in today's values) was offered by Queen Anne's government in 1714 to anyone who could devise a way of fixing a ship's longitude to within 30 nautical miles after sailing for 6 weeks across the Atlantic.

The Board consisted of many August Persons: the Speaker of the House of Commons, the First Lord of the Admiralty, the Astronomer Royal, the President of the Royal Society, the First Commissioner of Trade, the Savilian, Lucasian (in 1663 Henry Lucas bequeathed £100 to Cambridge to found a lectureship in Mathematics), and Plumian Professors of Mathematics at the Universities of Oxford and Cambridge, were empanelled. The first suggestion that ships be moored at intervals across the Atlantic to let off cannons and fire rockets to indicate the time did not meet with approval.

The board next met 28 years later to consider the work of a Yorkshire carpenter-turned-clockmaker named John Harrison. In 1726, at the age of 33, he had made a wooden-cogged clock using lignum vitae as it was somewhat oily. Lubricating oil could not be used as it clogged up and, likewise, metal gears could not be used. His clock was the most accurate in the world at the time, gaining or losing no more than a second a month. He calibrated his clocks by noting the precise time it took star for a to disappear behind a neighbour's chimney stack.

In 1737 Harrison came to London and obtained an interview with Sir Edmund Halley, the Astronomer Royal. H1 kept time to within 10 seconds a day, not accurate enough. H2 followed in two years, but not until 1752 did he produce H4, his most famous watch, measuring 5 inches across, with jewelled bearings and a balance wheel with a bimetallic anchor point to compensate for temperature changes, and Harrison's Going Barrel, a mechanism enabling the clock to be wound up without stopping it.

In 1761 H4 was carried by John Harrison's son, William, to Jamaica on board HMS *Deptford*. An account of this journey appeared in a letter John Harrison wrote to an MP: 'In sailing to the Madeiras, Mr. Harrison acquainted Capt. Diggs with the exact time he would see the island of Porto Santo; which, had they trusted to the ship's reckoning, they would never have seen at all, which would have been a great inconvenience as they were in Want of Beer.'

When HMS *Deptford* reached Jamaica, calculations showed that the difference between land-based measurements and H4 amounted to little more than a mile. Still the Board did not pay up, demanding proof that Harrison's design could be copied. Unfortunately for Harrison, Halley had been succeeded by Rev. Nevil Maskelyne as Astronomer Royal. Maskelyne was out of sympathy with Harrison as he was keen to use the Moon to determine longitude, and, dare it be said, was anxious to collect the prize money himself.

In 1764, an expedition to Barbados was mounted, with Maskelyne, John Harrison and his son William. A year later when all the calculations had been made, H4 was found to be just 39 seconds out after the voyage from England, equivalent to an error of 9.8 nautical miles, just one-third of the error needed to win the prize. Yet still the Board did not pay up. Bureaucratic wrangling came to the attention of King George III, who gave audience to William Harrison (John was now 79) in 1772.

On hearing the whole sorry tale, the king is said to have muttered 'These people have been cruelly wronged. By God, Harrison, I will see you righted.'

The King, together with his own private astronomer, and Harrison, checked H5 every day and found it to be true to one-third of a second a day. The parliamentarian, Edmund Burke, spoke up for Harrison and he was eventually rewarded with the prize, which had been reduced to £10,000 – every conceivable deduction having been made by a parsimonious Government.

Harrison's final vindication came when Captain James Cook took Larcum Kendall's copy of H4 (he charged £450 for this – equivalent at today's prices of £20,000) on his second voyage of exploration of the Pacific. Cook, though at first sceptical, was won over.

James **Cook** (1728-1779) was the son of an agricultural labourer and farm bailiff, born at the Yorkshire village of Marston, the second of eight children. He was 6 feet tall, with piercing brown eyes, and described as earnest, studious and quick-witted. He wrote 'I had ambition not only to go farther than anyone had been before, but as far as it was possible for Man to go.' At the age of 12 he was apprenticed to a shipowner at Whitby, Yorkshire, and was involved in the coal trade from Newcastle to Norway and the Baltic.

At the age of 27 he joined the Royal Navy and after four years' service was appointed Master. He was obsessed with his crew's health, insisting upon a diet of fruit and vegetables, and believed that indigenous people should be treated with respect. He surveyed the St Lawrence River to Quebec, making possible the passage of the English Fleet with the English army. Under the command of Sir James Wolfe, they defeated the French on the Heights of Abraham at Quebec on 13 September 1759. A year later the French army surrendered at Montreal and Canada was ceded to Great Britain by the Peace of Paris, 1763.

Cook was later appointed surveyor of Newfoundland and Labrador. He came to the attention of the Royal Society for his report of the total eclipse of the Sun on 5 August 1766. His charts were the only ones of the time that were not regarded as a menace to navigators. He was able to calculate longitude as well as latitude, a rare ability in those days.

In 1768 the Royal Society petitioned King George III to send a ship to observe the transit of Venus, which could be used to determine the Astronomical Unit, the distance of the Earth from the Sun, upon which all other astronomical measurements depend. It was thought that the AU could be calculated if the precise time that Venus crossed the Sun's disc were known. Cook was appointed to lead this expedition.

While en route he was ordered to open secret orders which charged him to research and map the South Pacific Ocean, and if possible, identify Terra Australis Incognita, an unknown Southern land first seen by the Dutch explorer Tasman about 1644. These orders may well have had a political purpose, that it to say, to annex territories to prevent the Dutch or French doing this.

Cook had set sail on 25 August 1778 with a year's provisions on the 14-gun 370 ton converted Whitby collier *Endeavour*, together with the botanist and artist Joseph **Banks**, several scientists and a crew of 85 (of whom only 45 returned), including 13 Royal Marines. There were 17 sheep, 4 pigs, 3 cats (to catch the rats), and a milking goat. There were also numerous ducks and chickens, most of which got washed overboard in the Bay of Biscay on the outward voyage.

It was about a month prior to departure, that the Admiralty informed Cook that a certain Joseph Banks, Esq., aged 25, a member of the Royal Society and possessed of a large fortune, well versed in Natural History, would be accompanying him, together with his 'suite', consisting of 8 persons and their 'baggage'. They comprised 2 Swedish naturalists, 2 artists, 2 footmen, and 2 black servants, together with his greyhound and his spaniel. Banks paid £10,000 for this privilege, equivalent to about £600,000 in today's money. History does not record Cook's thoughts with regard to this arrangement.

He sailed westwards round Cape Horn and landed at Tahiti, recently discovered by Wallis, on 13 April 13th 1769. For some reason the observation of the transit of Venus was not successful. However, in company with the native Tahitian, Prince Tupia, who was to be his servant, navigator, and interpreter, he sailed westwards and encountered the land of the Long White Cloud, Aotearoa, now known as New Zealand, on 6 October 1779. It had been seen previously by Tasman but he had not landed. Tupia was able to speak to the natives (Maoris) in their own language, remarkably, as they were over 2,500 miles distant, an example of the Polynesian diaspora. Tupia was to die later in disease-ridden Batavia, now Jakarta, along with many of Cook's crew.

Cook circumnavigated the North Island, proving that it was in fact an Island, and charted it. He landed at Queen Charlotte's Sound, planting a Union Jack and claiming the land in the name of King George III (this was subsequently repudiated by the Government). He charted 2,400 miles of the New Zealand coastline in 3 months, a remarkable feat. He then set sail for Australia, landing in Botany Bay on 28 April 28th 1770, encountering great hostility from the natives. Understandably in view of their subsequent history. Joseph Banks came away with over 400 specimens of new plants, naming a Genus of Australian shrubs. He was later knighted and became President of the Royal Society.

On his voyage northwards, on 11 June 1770, the *Endeavour* ran on to the coral of the Great Barrier Reef sustaining a large hole which the ship's pumps could only just cope with. All the heavy furniture, guns and anchor were thrown overboard in an attempt to lighten the ship, and on the second high tide she floated clear, the hole being patched with a sail. She was then beached at the place Cook called Cape Tribulation, now a destination of many 'backpackers'. It was at this point that they saw their first kangaroo. Banks shot one, cooked it and pronounced it 'excellent'.

On his third and final voyage Cook, now aged 51, landed at Waimea, Kauai, which he named the Sandwich Islands, and was killed by a native over a dispute over a stolen ship's boat. He was later buried at sea and the news of his death took nearly a year to reach England

These voyages of exploration were motivated entirely by the altruistic quest for knowledge, in true scientific spirit, and James Cook, with his talent for observation and recording, as well as his ability as a seafarer, was clearly the right man for the task.

Cook was elected a Fellow of the Royal Society in 1776. It is interesting to note that his activities were responsible for the greater part of the establishment of the British Empire in Canada, Australia and New Zealand. First came the explorers, then the soldiers, then the traders.

Clocks and watches had become reliable and popular by 1797 and Parliament decided, in its wisdom, that both their possession and manufacture should be taxed. This resulted in the almost total destruction of the industry with widespread unemployment, until thankfully the tax was withdrawn in 1798.

For four years, from Christmas 1872 until May 1876, HMS *Challenger* surveyed the world's oceans. *Challenger* was a wooden corvette of 2,300 tons, the first steamship to cross the Antarctic Circle. The world's deepest ocean, 10,800 metres (35,640 feet), was discovered in the Marianas Trench off the island of Mindanao in the Phillipines – the ***Challenger Deep***. This was deeper than Mount Everest is high, at 8,850 metres (29,035 feet). At this depth, the water pressure is 10 tons per-square inch, and fish found there tend to explode on being brought to the surface, rendering their description and classification difficult. The findings of HMS *Challenger* were later published in 80 volumes.

Admiralty navigation charts became regarded as the most accurate and comprehensive and were generally in use worldwide. Thus, when the Meridian Conference was convened in Washington in 1884, it was agreed that The Prime Meridian, Longitude $0^{\circ}0''$, should pass through Greenwich, where an

Observatory had been set up in 1675. The French, however, disagreed, as they wanted the Prime Meridian to go through Paris. In 1911, 26 years later, they finally accepted the decision of the Meridian Conference.

In addition, at this conference the International Time Zones were defined. There were to be 24 zones (±12) and each zone included 15 degrees of longitude: 360÷24=15. Just as well the Chaldeans divided the circle into 360 degrees and the day into 24 hours.

CHAPTER THREE

ASTRONOMY

To belong, to create, to communicate, and to explore are instinctive behaviour patterns of many animals, particularly the higher primates such as Man. Curiosity is a manifestation of the desire to explore, to discover the significance of our relationship with the external world.

The Chaldeans of Babylon climbed their *Ziggurat* – the Tower of Babel (Genesis 11, v. 3–9) was a Ziggurat – and observed the stars, brilliant in the desert night sky. Ziggurats were usually great mounds of sun-dried brick with a coating of glazed brick or tile. Sometimes they had flat terraces like a step pyramid and sometimes an inclined plane to the top, rather like the famous Giralda in Seville, Spain, built in the twelfth century. The best known Ziggurat was at the city of Ur, in Mesopotamia, between the Rivers Tigris and Euphrates, now part of Iraq. There, remains have been found dating as far back as 3,500BC. Thus began the association of altitude with status and sanctity, as there was usually a shrine on top. This was about the reign of King **Nebuchadnezzar** (605–562BC). So began *Astronomy* – the naming of stars; hence many stars have Arabic names.

Groups of stars were thought to resemble animals, perhaps related to the tribal totem (see Chapter 10) hence the constellations. They used a duodecimal system, with the number 12 (6 is the 'perfect number' the product of 1, 2 and 3) as a basis, and divided the sky into 12 zones, the Signs of the *Zodiac*. They divided a circle into 360 degrees, a day into 24 hours, an hour into 60 minutes, and a minute into 60 seconds.

It is possible that many of the ancient monoliths and stone circles, the most famous of which in Britain is *Stonehenge*, were primitive calendars, used to provide a datum point which could be used for agricultural purposes, and to predict that most dramatic and terrifying occurrence, a total eclipse of the Sun. An Ancient priest who could do that was clearly a man of great power and influence. A collection of Chinese Documents called the Shu King reveals a tragic tale of two Chinese official astronomers, Hsi and Ho, who failed to 'perform the rites associated with an eclipse of the Sun', presumably to predict it, and were put to death. This eclipse has been dated to 2136BC. Clearly there was considerable pressure to get the sums right with more accurate methods.

Unfortunately the Ancient Britons (1750BC) at that time had not made that extraordinary evolutionary leap, the association between sounds and visual images, that led to the development of writing, so we have no record of their thoughts, activities or findings. Not so the civilisations of the Eastern Mediterranean. Those priestly writings, the heiroglyphics in the tombs of the Pharoahs of ancient Egypt, led to the notion of an alphabet, developed further by the ancient Greeks, who improved on the Babylonian observations.

Greek astronomy was founded by **Thales** in the sixth century BC, but the Greek, **Hipparchus** (ca.146–126BC), could well be described as the father of modern astronomy. He observed on the island of Rhodes and catalogued 1080 stars and classified their magnitudes, a logarithmic scale from 1 to 6, the 6th being just discernable with the naked eye.

He invented trigonometry and established the notion of coordinates of latitude and longitude as a method of locating position on the Earth's surface. The stars were located by their *declination* and *right ascension*. The declination is the equivalent of latitude and is the angular distance, north or south, of the celestial equator, measured in degrees. The right ascension is the equivalent of longitude and is measured in hours, minutes and seconds, eastwards from an arbitrary zero or starting point, the intersection of the celestial equator with the *ecliptic*, the First Point of Aries. The ecliptic is the region of the sky through which the Earth and the planets appear to pass. It is called this because eclipses of the Sun or Moon occur when the Moon's orbit crosses it. It lies in the equatorial plane of the Sun. It is interesting to note that any point in the universe can be located by two coordinates, an angle and an interval of time.

In 130BC Hipparchus discovered and measured the **precession of the equinoxes**, the fact that the axis of the Earth wobbles a bit in its rotation, moving in a circle with a period of about 26,000 years. The Phoenicians, who were great traders and used the stars for navigation, no doubt brought the information to the Greeks (they also invented money). Hipparchus also fixed the lengths of the solar and sidereal years, the months, the synodic periods (the mean interval of time between successive conjunctions of a pair of planets) of the 5 planets.

His predecessor **Eratosthenes** (276–196BC) determined the obliquity of the plane of the Earth's orbit to the plane of the ecliptic at 23°. This varies between 22 and 24°. By geometry he determined the circumference of the Earth. This is how he did it: Alexandria and Syene in Egypt lie on the same meridian, and were 5000 stadia apart. When the Sun was vertically overhead at Syene it appeared 7°12' South at Alexandria (he must have used a signalling system to synchronise these observations). Calculation made the circumference of the Earth to be 252,000 stadia, equivalent to 25,000 miles – quite close to modern estimations at 24,000 miles.

The next famous name in the history of astronomy is that of **Ptolemy** (Claudius Ptolemaeus of Alexandria). His dates are uncertain but he lived in the second century AD and worked in Alexandria from AD127–151). He is not to be confused with the Egyptian Ptolemies, one of whom was Cleopatra's brother.

Ptolemy wrote a book called the *Almagest*, in 8 volumes, giving the coordinates for some 8,000 places, concerning astronomy, mathematics and geography, and developed Hipparchus's plane and spherical trigonometry, giving tables of chords and sines, mathematical constants, of great accuracy. Ptolemy established a value for π (pi), the ratio of the circumference to the diameter of a circle (3.1416...), and was the first to project a sphere on to a plane.

Unfortunately he made a serious error in the circumference of the Earth and navigational charts were inaccurate by a factor of about 2. Hence Christopher Columbus's error in thinking he had reached India (or China) when in fact he had only got to

America. He devised a complex system of cycles, epicycles and deferents in order to explain the motions of the planets, assuming the Earth was the centre of the universe, a notion that persisted until Copernicus and Galileo proved that the Sun was the centre of the solar system and the Earth rotated on its axis.

Alexandria was founded by Alexander the Great in 332BC as a naval base. Its great library was founded in 295BC, and held some 700,000 scrolls, before it was finally destroyed by the Christians in AD389. Plutarch wrote that Julius Caesar, in 48BC, became enamoured of Cleopatra and was therefore on her side. 'When the enemy tried to cut off his fleet, Caesar was forced to repel the danger by using fire, which spread from the dockyards and destroyed the Great Library.' Thus many of the original Greek texts were lost, including plays by Aristophanes, Sophocles, and Euripedes, one of the greatest tragedies to delay the progress of civilisation, which then entered a dark age of scientific enquiry.

Along with Ptolemy, many other famous mathematicians worked at Alexandria, Euclid, Archimedes, Aristarchus, and Erastothenes, concluding that the Earth revolved around the Sun. Here, seventy scholars translated the Pentateuch of the Old Testament from Hebrew into Greek – the Septuagint. Herophilus dissected the human body and recognised that that the brain and not the heart is the seat of intelligence. The Christians destroyed the pagan temple of Sarapeum, which housed a daughter branch of the Great Library. A twelfth century account of the Arab conquest of Egypt in AD642 states that the bathhouses of Alexandria were heated for 6 months with burning scrolls.

Happily, the Great Library, the Biblotheca Alexandrina, is being resurrected (2001), under the auspices of the United Nations Educational and Scientific Organisation (UNESCO), designed by a group of architects from the Norwegian firm of Snöhetta, which won a global architectural competition for the design at a cost of over US$172,000,000.

Mahomet captured Mecca in AD630 and founded the religion of Islam. Mahomet was firm that Islam was not to be a religion of miracles and personalities, rather of analysis and contemplation, and this suited the progress of science. No representation of people or animals was permitted by Islam, hence their architecture is largely confined to geometrical patterns and designs.

Alexandria was captured by Omar in AD641, leading to the extinction of Greek astronomy and its reappearance 150 years later on the banks of the Tigris. In AD800 the Caliph of Baghdad, Haroun-al-Rashid, ordered a translation of the *Almagest*, and in 829 an observatory was built in Baghdad.

In 813 the Caliph Mamoun (Al-Mamun – 'in whom men trust') founded a college at Khorasan to promote the study of literature and science. He ordered the works of Euclid to be translated from Greek into Arabic and founded observatories in Baghdad and Khassium by which the inclination of the ecliptic could be measured.

Ptolemy's tables were confirmed and eclipses of the Sun were correctly predicted for AD977 and AD978. In AD1420 an observatory was founded at Samarkand by Ulugh Beg a grandson of Tamerlane.

Arab astronomy was introduced into Spain by the Moors and reappeared in Cordoba and Toledo, and tables were published in AD1252 under the authority of Alfonso X of Castile.

In 1256 a Yorkshireman, John **Holywood**, published a textbook of spherical astronomy known as *Sacro Bosco*, which went into 59 editions.

In 1543 the Polish priest Nicolaus Koppernigk (1473–1544) (**Copernicus**) having studied the works of Hipparchus, published his book *De Revolutionibus Orbium Coelestium*, with some diffidence, as it was heretical, late in his life. Unfortunately he had a fatal stroke and was unable to see the revolution in thought that his work was to lead to, overturning the Ptolemaic geocentric world and suggesting that the Sun was in fact the centre of the solar system, and that the apparent motion of the heavens was due to the Earth rotating on its own axis. Although Copernicus was Polish by birth he studied law and medicine, as well as theology, in Padua, in what is now northern Italy. By then printing had been developed and it became possible to disseminate ideas widely.

1564 saw the birth of both William Shakespeare and Galileo Galilei. **Galileo** (1564–1642) was appointed professor of mathematics at Padua. In 1609, using lenses devised by two Flemish spectacle makers Lippershey and Janssen, he constructed the first telescope, giving a magnification of about 10x. He later improved it to 30x and started looking at the stars and planets. He built the apparatus, he did the experiment, he published the result and must be considered the first scientist of the modern age. What he saw was startling indeed – the four satellites of the planet Jupiter, revolving around that planet – and in particular the phases of Venus, thus giving experimental confirmation of Copernicus' ideas, and suggesting that the geocentric notion was incorrect.

Galileo, in spite of advice to the contrary and his earlier agreement not to do so, published his work *Dialogo dei due massimi sisteme del monde* in January 1632, to great acclaim. He believed that Truth was more important than Authority and of course he was mistaken. ('Tell the Truth and get your head bashed in' – old Hungarian proverb).

In August of that year sale of the book was prohibited and in October Galileo was summoned to Rome to appear before the Inquisition. He was now 70, almost blind, and pleaded illness and infirmity, but no excuses were permitted. He arrived in February 1633 but was not examined until 21 June, and was interrogated under threats of torture. He recanted the next day and was sentenced to incarceration (house arrest), and by way of penance was told to recite once a week for three years the seven penitential psalms.

Perhaps he rose from his knees and said *'Eppur si muove'* ('yet it does move') – this was heresy, as the doctrine of the Church at the time was to follow the Greek philosopher **Aristotle** (384–322 BC, disciple of Plato and tutor to Alexander the Great) who put the Earth motionless at the centre of the universe, which consisted of two parts: The Cosmos (Greek: *kosmos* – the world) contained the Moon, the Sun, the planets, and the stars moving around the Earth. All motion in the Cosmos was circular, perfect, hence there could be no beginning and no end. The other part was the sublunar world (the phrase can still be seen on ancient tombstones), where vertical and horizontal motion was permitted, hence beginnings and endings, the world we inhabit. The Catholic Church adopted this philosophy rigorously, dissent was heresy, which could mean death.

At any rate Galileo was freed and spent the last eight years of his life in seclusion in Florence. He continued to work, however, and thought out the idea of using the pendulum to regulate a clock, realised by Huygens fifteen years later. Thus the dominance of Italian science ended with this example of political (in this instance religious) correctness. Science then moved to England (**Newton**) and Holland (**Huygens** – who identified the rings of Saturn).

Here is the background to the situation. Europe at that time was a dangerous place. On 31 October 1517 Martin **Luther** had posted on the door of the Castle Church in Wittenburg his 95 Theses. This was a document criticising the Catholic Church's sale of Indulgences, a practice whereby forgiveness of sin and atonement could be obtained by giving money to the Church, possibly to help rebuild St Peter's Basilica in the Vatican. This led to an attempt by the Pope to excommunicate Luther. However the Holy Roman Emperor Charles V refused to comply and the rift with the Pope was complete. This was the beginning of the Reformation, Catholics versus Protestants.

In England, Henry VIII had written a thesis '*Assertio Septem Sacramentorum adversus Martinus Lutherus*' (Defence of the Seven Sacraments) and the Pope, Leo X, conferred on him the title *Fidei Defensor* (Defender of the Faith). This was later revoked. Henry split with the Roman Catholic Church as the Pope refused to grant him a divorce from Catherine of Aragon, who had failed to produce a male child. Henry wished to marry Anne Boleyn, who was pregnant at the time. The title was confirmed by Parliament in 1544 and has been used by English monarchs since, with the initials F.D. appearing on English coins to this very day. With the execution of his Chancellor, Sir Thomas More, numerous other priests, and the Dissolution of the Monasteries in 1535, the rift with Rome was complete and the Church of England (Anglican) was established.

The Spanish Inquisition had been established in 1478 by a Papal Bull granted to the Catholic Monarchs by Pope Sixtus IV. It had much to do with anti-Semitism as the Jews in Spain had become increasingly wealthy and influential. The *Auto-da-fé* (Act of Faith) was a spectacular tribunal established to deal with those found guilty of heresy by the Inquisition. Galileo was one of its victims. Another was the Italian philosopher Giordano **Bruno**, who believed in an infinite universe and that planets revolved around stars. He was accused of heresy and burnt at the stake in 1600.

Two of Galileo's contemporaries were Tycho **Brahe**, (1546–1601) a Danish astronomer, and Johannes **Kepler** (1571–1630). The three corresponded regularly. Under Tycho's guidance a magnificent observatory was constructed at Uraniborg and for 21 years he observed, measured and catalogued the planets and stars. With a new king of Denmark he lost his royal patronage and moved to Prague under the patronage of the Emperor Rudolph II. He moved his instruments there and was joined by Kepler in 1600. He died in 1601 and Kepler inherited his catalogue of observations as well as his position as Imperial Mathematician, though at a reduced salary.

The Emperor was more interested in ***astrology*** however, and Kepler's first work was a horoscope of the Emperor. In his early years Kepler made a living as an astrologer. Astrology has something in common with hypnosis, the basis of which is: belief plus expectation plus misdirected attention. In the case of astrology, the misdirected attention is directed to the conjunctions of the planets. In the case of palmistry it is to the lines on hands. In the case of acupuncture it is to needle pricks. In aromatherapy it is to smells. Practitioners of these Arts (they are not sciences) need to have persuasive and convincing personalities, and to be able to tell people what they want to hear.

Kepler eventually produced the Rudolphine Tables, of an accuracy that led them to be the best available for a hundred years. Kepler showed that the orbit of the planet Mars was an ellipse (this more accurate estimation helped to discredit the old Ptolemaic system of cycles and epicycles and supported Galileo's ideas), and postulated laws that related the periodicity of the

planets to their distance from the Sun. His work was interrupted in 1620 because his mother was arrested in Wurttemburg on
a charge of witchcraft. Fortunately, due to Kepler's efforts she
was acquitted after 13 months' imprisonment. The last ladies to
be hanged for witchcraft in England were Temperance Lloyd and
Susannah Edwards, in 1682, and Alice Molland in 1685, hanged
at Heavitree, Exeter, Devon. A memorial plaque to their names
is in the gardens of the remains of the Rougement Castle in
Exeter 'in the hope of an end to persecution and intolerance'
...and, one might add, superstition.

Kepler is best known for his 3 Laws:

1. Each planet moves in an ellipse with the Sun at one
focus.

2. The line joining the orbiting body to the parent body
sweeps out equal areas in equal times.

3. The square of the siderial periods are proportional to the
cube of the mean distances apart of the orbiting and parent
bodies. T^2 over R^3 is constant – more accurately a correction
should be applied to take into account the difference in the
masses of the bodies.

The contribution of Isaac **Newton** (1642–1727) to astronomy,
using his Law of Universal Gravitation, made it possible to predict the movements of planets, and led to the discovery of the
planets Neptune, Uranus and Pluto. Neptune was discovered by
J.G. **Galle** at the Berlin Observatory on 23 September 1846 following predictions made independently by John Couch **Adams**
in England and U.J.J. **Leverrier** in France.
Uranus was discovered by William **Herschel** in 1781 and
Pluto was discovered by Clyde **Tombaugh** at the Lowell
Observatory on 18 February 1930 – although Pluto and its com-
panion Charon are so small as not to have any gravitational
effect on Neptune and Uranus – the Gas Giants. Newton's mathematical methods explained why Keplers' laws were correct. His

colleague and mentor Edmund **Halley** (1656–1742) charted the movement of a comet which had appeared in November 1682 and predicted, correctly, it would return 75 years later, based on previous observations. It reappeared on 12 March 1759. Halley had persuaded Newton to publish his *Principia Mathematica.*

Newton constructed a reflecting telescope, which overcame the problem of chromatic aberration, a distortion due to the fact that light of different wavelengths is refracted differently by a medium such as the glass used in lenses.

Newton also contributed to mathematics by his discovery of the *calculus*, which he called fluxions. Though it should be noted that the German philosopher and mathematician Gottfried **Leibnitz** (1646–1716) also discovered the calculus independently and possibly earlier than Newton. Leibnitz's notation was adopted in Europe, but somewhat reluctantly in England. A forty-year feud existed between the two. Leibnitz believed that we inhabit the best of all possible worlds, a philosophy disputed by the French writer Voltaire in his book *Candide*. Newton also contributed to the science of *optics*, demonstrating the splitting of light into its component colours using a prism – the solar *spectrum* (Latin: *spectrum* – a ghost). Newton was a believer in the corpuscular theory of light, that it consisted of tiny particles moving with colossal speed, as against Huygens, who thought it consisted of waves.

In 1801 the English scientist Thomas **Young** showed that, if a narrow beam of light was passed through two adjacent holes on to a screen, a series of bands of light with alternate dark patches, appeared, suggesting that light was a wave motion. From the width of the bands it was possible to calculate the wavelength of light – red light was about 750 nanometers and violet light about 390 nanometers (3900 Ångströms – a notation that should probably be abandoned. **Ångström** was a Swedish astronomer who identified hydrogen in the Sun by its characteristic Fraunhofer lines, in 1862).

In 1766 the German astronomer J. **Titius** proposed a relationship between the relative distances of the planets from the Sun. In 1772 this was published by J.E. **Bode** and is known as Bode's Law. This stated that the proportionate distances of the several planets from the Sun may be represented by adding 4 to each term of the series –0–3–6–12–24. There is a discrepancy in that 0 should be $1^1/_2$. Also it does not work for Neptune and Pluto. There was a gap at 2.8AU where a planet should have been.

In 1801 the Italian astronomer Guiseppe **Piazzi** identified an object in this location. He called it *Ceres* in honour of the patron Goddess of Sicily, where his telescope was located at Palermo. It was dim and small and he first thought it was a comet but its orbit proved it was nearly circular. This was the first *asteroid*. Many more have since been found constituting the asteroid belt. They are either the remains of a planet which has been broken up by the gravitational field of the planet Jupiter, or of a planet which had never coalesced. Jupiters' gravitational field is so immense that it acts as a cosmic dustbin, attracting wandering objects such as comets, where it devours them. This was observed in July 1994 when the comet *Shoemaker-Levy* 9 broke up into 22 fragments prior to entering Jupiter, where black splodges marked its demise. The small irregular moons of Mars, Phobos and Deimos, are probably captured asteroids.

The Earth is constantly bombarded with material from outer space. Tiny fragments burn up in the upper atmosphere and are visible as *meteors*. Larger fragments descend to Earth as *meteorites*. Trajectories of meteorites have been plotted which show that they originate in the asteroid belt. Examination of meteorites gives evidence of the origin and evolution of the solar system. There are 3 types of meteorites, depending on their composition:

1. Stony meteorites (aerolites) 90%. Further divided into chondrites and achondrites depending on the presence of chondrules, which are small (1mm) inclusions, which may be metal or silicates. The chemical composition of chondrites is similar to the atmosphere of the Sun, except that there is no free hydrogen or helium. Carbonaceous chondrites contain carbon. Some are altered by the presence of water up to 20%. They date from 4.5 billion years ago, hence their composition reflects that at the origin of the solar system

2. Stony-iron (siderolites or lithosiderites), containing a higher proportion of iron, with free metal and stone in equal proportion. The stones are olivines, pyroxines and feldspars, similar to Moon rock.

3. Siderites, with a high proportion of iron and nickel.

Large asteroids can cause catastrophic damage. Evidence suggests that the nickel mine in Sudbury, Ontario, Canada was the remains of a giant asteroid that collided with Earth about 2 billion years ago.

The Canyon Diablo meteorite in Arizona, which fell 40,000 years ago, caused a crater 1.2km in diameter. A 10km diameter asteroid, by virtue of its dust storm, would cause total obliteration of sunlight. Evidence suggests that a such an asteroid collided with Earth about 65 million years ago at Chicxulub, Mexico, travelling at 30km/sec, causing a crater 100km wide and 12km deep, and may well have been the cause of the mass extinction at the end of the Cretaceous Period, and the demise of the dinosaurs. It is thought that mass extinctions, of which there have been several in the history of the Earth, have been due to asteroid collisions.

In 1814 Joseph von **Fraunhofer**, a German optician, passed light through a slit and then through an accurately made prism and found that the solar spectrum was crossed by many dark lines. He named these A, in the red end, to K in the violet end. Thus the lines of sodium are in the D band. He recorded over 700. In 1842 these were photographed by the French physicist Alexandre Edmand **Becquerel** and this technique has greatly increased our knowledge. Over 30,000 Fraunhofer lines have been recorded and their wavelengths measured.

In 1859, the German chemists R.W. **Bunsen** and G.R. **Kirchhoff** worked out a system for identifying chemical elements by heating them and comparing their spectral lines – the spectroscope. Caesium and rubidium were discovered by this method. In 1868, Sir Norman **Lockyer** identified the gas, helium (Greek: *helios* – sun) by its characteristic lines, which had not been seen before. The gas, not identified on Earth until 1890 by Sir William Ramsey, was found to be given off by compounds containing uranium. It is present in the atmosphere to the extent of 50 parts per million, and up to 7% of natural gas wells. The 'red shift' that is to say, the movement of the Fraunhofer lines towards the red or longer wavelengths, is a measure of the recession of a star or galaxy from us, using the Doppler principle.

The Austrian physicist Christian Johann **Doppler** in 1842 showed that the frequency of a wave diminishes as the source is moving away, and increases as the source approaches. He placed the trumpet section of the local band in a railway truck and told them to play a continuous note. When the train went past the observers it was noted that the pitch fell as the train receded.

In 1848 the French physicist Armand Hippolyte Louis **Fizeau** suggested that the Doppler effect could be adapted to spectral lines and used to measure the relative motions of the stars and galaxies with respect to Earth – the Doppler-Fizeau effect. Using this technique, in 1929 the American astronomer Edwin **Hubble** found that the velocities of receding galaxies was proportional to their distance from us – Hubble's Law – demonstrating an expanding universe.

In 1868 Sirius (8.7 light years away) was found to be receding at 29 miles/second. In 1890 Arcturus was found to be approaching at 3.75 miles/second. In 1912 M31, the great Spiral Nebula in Andromeda, at a distance from Earth of 2.3 million light years, was found to be approaching our Galaxy, the Milky Way, at 125 miles/second. Recent measurements put this at 200 miles/second. An intragalactic collision is predicted within 2 billion years. 13 out of 15 galaxies were found to be receding.

In 1781 the French astronomer Charles **Messier** (1730–1817) catalogued 103 *nebulae*. The word nebulous means diffuse, or ill-defined. These appeared as small patches of luminous fog, and, with increasing resolving power of telescopes, have been classified as intragalactic – within our galaxy (the Milky Way), or extragalactic, outside our galaxy. Intragalactic nebulae are further classified as:

1. Diffuse, gaseous.
2. Planetary, open clusters and globular clusters.

The **Pleiades** (M45, the Seven Sisters) in the constellation of Taurus the Bull, is a cluster of 500 stars, 410 light years away, with a diameter of 550 light years, with seven bright stars. The extragalactic spiral nebula in Andromeda, M31, NGC224, was first observed by the German astronomer Simon **Marius** in 1612. It is the only nebula to be visible with the naked eye and the most distant object.

The Orion nebula (M42, M43) was first observed by Christian Huygens in 1656. In 1924 the American astronomer Edwin Hubble used a 100-inch telescope at Mount Wilson to determine the distance of M31 using cepheid variables, and found it to be more than 1 million light years away, far outside our own galaxy. More accurate measurements put the distance at 2.3 million light years. The resolving power of the extra-terrestrial Hubble telescope, launched in April 1990, is 7 milli-seconds of arc and many extragalactic nebulae have been identified.

In 1850 the English mathematician Norman Robert **Pogson** devised a numerical system for determining the magnitude of planets and stars. This involved dividing Hipparchus's 6 categories into units of 100, $\sqrt[6]{100} = 2.512$. Thus every unit is 2.512 more or less than the next one; magnitude 2 would be 2.512 times less than magnitude 1. The Sun comes out at magnitude -26, the full Moon at -11, Sirius at -1.5. These are apparent magnitudes. Absolute magnitudes are those assumed from a distance of 10 parsecs (The parallax second is the distance at which an object would have an annual parallax of one arc-second – about 3.26 light years or 3×10^{13} kilometres). The Sun comes out at 4.8 on this scale. Previously magnitudes had been given designations according to the Greek alphabet, alpha α being the brightest, omega (Ω) the dimmest, in a constellation.

Measurement being one of the objects of science, it was necessary to measure (a) the Astronomical Unit (AU), the average distance of the Earth from the Sun, upon which all other calculations are based, and (b) the velocity of light. The AU was determined using the method of *parallax*, the apparent displacement when observations are made from two different points, whose distance apart is known, against a fixed background. The first attempt was made in 1673 by the French astronomers J.D. **Cassini** (who observed a break in the rings of Saturn known as Cassini's division) in Paris, and J. **Richer** in Cayenne, French Guiana, using simultaneous observations of the planet Mars, when Mars and Earth were aligned, against a background of stars. Their baseline was 10,000km, the distance between Paris and Cayenne. They arrived at a figure of 87 million miles, 7% less than the current figure, which was established in 1931, using the asteroid Eros. This is about 93 million miles. The AU can be calculated from these observations using Kepler's Laws. Because the orbit of the Earth is not a perfect circle, being elliptical, the actual distance varies from 91.4 to 94.6 million miles.

Once the AU had been determined, it became possible to measure the distance of stars from Earth. By the nineteenth century precision engineering and the stability of telescopes had developed to such an extent that the German Astronomer F. **Bessell** was able to measure the parallax of a star, the baseline being twice the AU, observations being made with an interval of 6 months. In 1838 he found that the parallax of the Star 61 Cygni was 0.31 of an arc-second, making its distance 10 light years. In 1840 the Russian astronomer W. **Struve** found Vega to be 13 light years away, and about the same time the Scottish Astronomer Thomas **Henderson**, working at the Cape of Good Hope, found alpha Centauri to be a mere 4 light years away, our nearest star but one.

Galileo attempted to measure the velocity of light, unsuccessfully. The first serious attempt was made by the Danish astronomer Olaus **Roemer** in 1676. He measured the difference in time that eclipses of the Moons of Jupiter occurred when Jupiter was moving towards the Earth than when it was moving away, knowing the width of the Earth's orbit. He estimated a figure of 132,000 miles per second. More accurate measurements were made in 1849 by the French physicist A.H.L. **Fizeau** who used a light beam, passing through the cogs of a rotating wheel to a mirror 5 miles away, and reflected back. When the interval between successive cogs permitted the light to be observed, from the speed of rotation of the wheel and the distance between the cogs and the distance the light had travelled, gave a measure of its velocity. He found it to be 196,000 miles per second, 5.2% too high. In 1850 the French physicist Jean **Foucault** used a rotating mirror and in 1862 found it to be 185,000 miles per second, 0.7% too low. Using the same technique, in the latter part of the nineteenth century, the American physicist Albert Abraham Michelson made it 186,271 miles per second in a vacuum, 0.006% too low. Present day measurements make it 186,282.3959 miles per second, 299,792.458 kilometres per second.

In 1912, the American astronomer Henrietta **Leavitt**, working at Harvard College Observatory, observed the yellow giant stars in the constellation Cepheus. These stars radiate 10,000 times as much energy as the Sun, and their brightness varies. The magnitude of delta Cephei varies between 3.6 and 4.3 in 5.4 days. She plotted the magnitude of a star in the Small Magellanic Cloud (a globular cluster) against its periodicity and established a period/luminosity curve. If the periodicity was measured, the luminosity could be calculated. If star A with a luminosity 4 times that of star B then it could be assumed that star B was twice as distant as star A. The difficulty was to establish the distance of a star from which the others could be calculated. The American astronomer Harlow **Shapley** found that a cepheid of absolute magnitude -2.3 had a luminosity of 5.96 days. This gave a yardstick from which other stars could be calculated. The Pole Star is a variable star with a period of 2.5 to 2.6 in 4 days.

Other variable stars are the eclipsing binaries such as Algol, and the ***pulsars***. The first pulsar, which is a source of rapidly interrupted radio waves, was found at the Mullard Radio Astronomy Observatory, Cambridge University, in 1968 by Jocelyn **Bell**, a graduate student, and Anthony **Hewitt** – at a wavelength of 3.7 metres (81MHz) and a pulse repetition frequency of 1.337 301 13 seconds. This was subsequently found to have come from the Crab Nebula, a Neutron Star, the remains of a supernova (a Star that had exploded on 4 July 1054).

Theory states that when a star of between 1.3 and 2 (?3) solar masses has exhausted its nuclear fuel (hydrogen mainly), it explodes as its radiation pressure outwards exceeds its gravitational attractive pressure inwards, it collapses under gravity and consists entirely of Neutrons.

It will then have a diameter of about 10 kilometres, with a density of 10^{17} tons per cubic metre (=100 million tons per cc). It then rotates emitting radio waves, light, and X-rays from its magnetic poles, as its electrons become photons and sweep across the universe like a lighthouse. The flashing beams were found in 1969, when astronomers knew what to look for.

The time interval between pulses varies from milliseconds in binary stars to 4 seconds. It is thought that more than half of all stars are in fact binary, rotating around a common centre of gravity. An *accretion disc* can develop between binary stars as matter streams between one star and the other, with the emission of X-rays. If one of the stars disintegrates, a nova is formed.

If the stars are aligned with the Earth, they form an eclipsing binary, the best known being *Algol* in the constellation Perseus, with a period of 69 hours. Algol (Arabic: ghoul in) was first identified as an eclipsing binary in 1782 by the English astronomer John **Goodricke**, a deaf-mute who died at the age of 22.

The properties of a neutron star were worked out in 1939 by J. Robert **Oppenheimer**, the American physicist. He was later appointed to supervise the *Manhattan Project*, which led to the development of the atomic bomb.

Should the exploding star have a mass greater than 3 solar masses, it will, according to present theory, become a *black hole*. This idea was introduced by the German physicist Karl **Schwarzchild** in 1916, after studying Einstein's relativity theory. The boundary of a black hole is called an *event horizon* and its radius depends on its mass, being about 3km times the mass of the body in solar units, the Sun being equal to 1. The theory is that the *escape velocity* (see below) of a black hole is greater than the velocity of light, so no radiation could escape. It is thought that there is a black hole revolving around the double star Cygnus X1 owing to its intense X-ray emission. There is evidence that a 'black hole' exists at the centre of M87 also at the centre of our galaxy, the Milky Way. Perhaps this would account for the relative stability of a galaxy.

Since gravitational force varies as the square of the distance from the centre of a mass such as the Earth, the higher a projectile rises the smaller is the attractive force. A rocket projected with an initial velocity of 6.98 miles per second would never return to Earth. This is the *escape velocity* for Earth. For the Moon, with a smaller mass, the escape velocity is 1.5 miles per second.

At a height of 35,788 kilometres (22,367 miles) a satellite will be in geostationary orbit, that is to say, its centrifugal outward force is exactly balanced by its inward gravitational force, and it will remain stationary over a fixed point on Earth. This is the **Clarke Belt**, named after the science fiction writer, Arthur C. Clarke, who worked out the mathematics of communication satellites in 1945, publishing an article in *Wireless World*. In 2003 there were 350 communication satellites in the Clarke Belt.

The gravitational force of the Earth is just sufficient to overcome the velocity of the thermal agitation of the atoms and molecules of the gases of the atmosphere, oxygen and nitrogen. (It is now thought that the primordial atmosphere consisted largely of carbon dioxide and nitrogen, transformed into oxygen by the action of organisms such as *cyanophytes*, the blue-green algae, found today in lichens, and *stromatolites*). So that, fortunately for us, the Earth has an atmosphere, unlike the Moon, Mercury or Mars. (Mars does have a very thin atmosphere – 1 millibar at the surface – of carbon dioxide). Venus, about the same size as Earth, has a dense atmosphere – 92 Bar at the surface, with a temperature of 735K – highly inhospitable for life, mainly of carbon dioxide, with water vapour and sulphuric acid drops on top.

There remain many unanswered questions with regard to the origin and nature of the universe – cosmology. One door opens, only to reveal many other doors closed.

CHAPTER FOUR
CHEMISTRY

The Science that is concerned with the composition of bodies and with the changes of composition they undergo.

Analytical Chemistry deals with methods of separation of purer substances from mixtures, of elements from compounds and with their estimation.

Synthetic Chemistry deals with the methods by which more complex substances can be built up from simpler ones.

The arrangement of atoms within a molecule, and the arrangement of molecules used to be regarded as the province of the chemist, while the physicist dealt with changes of state and motion of the molecules. This distinction can no longer be made and the two disciplines of Chemistry and Physics are progressively merging.

Between 10,000 and 100,000 years ago our ancestors discovered the use of fire. This was probably where there was a perpetual source of methane gas bubbling out of the Earth in what is now Armenia. In ancient mythology, Prometheus stole fire from the gods, and as a punishment was chained to a rock and had his liver pecked out by vultures by day. By night his liver grew again. Even in those days, it seems, people knew about the amazing recuperative powers of the liver.

Be that as it may, fire was used for cooking, to render cereals, fish, and meat more digestible and palatable. It was also used to heat clay for pottery, and to extract metals for the forging of weapons of war. But the most desirable of all metals was gold.

'We Spaniards suffer from a strange disease of the heart for which the only known remedy is gold' – said Hernando Cortes, who was a lawyer before he sought adventure by becoming a conquistador, demanding gold in tribute from the Aztec (Mexican) chieftain, Montezuma, in 1520. It is estimated that around 250,000 Aztecs died in pursuit of this objective. Spaniards were not alone in suffering from the disease; it is, regrettably, universal.

The delusion that alchemists suffered from was that base metals, such as lead or mercury, could be changed into gold. They never succeeded. In fact it was not until 1980, at a cost of $10,000 that a tiny particle of bismuth was converted into gold in the particle accelerator at the Lawrence Laboratory at the University of California in Berkeley.

One of the greatest challenges that faces Mankind is disposal of the radioactive chemical ***plutonium***, a by-product of uranium fission in nuclear reactors used for power generation. It is, like all heavy metals, intensely poisonous (toxic dose 160 nanograms) and radioactive (α-emitter) with a half-life of 26,000 years. It can also be used to make bombs, only 5kg is necessary, and there are many hundreds of tons scattered around the globe at present. If only it could be transformed into gold. The gold, provided it wasn't too radioactive, could then be sold to pay for the energy necessary to effect the transformation. Perhaps someone is working on it...

The Greek philosopher **Aristotle** (384–322BC) taught that there were four elements, Earth, Water (the sea), Air (the atmosphere) and Fire (invisible except during occasional flashes of lightning). The fifth element, or essence (Quintessence), he called aether. This was the purest, and in ancient philosophy formed the heavenly bodies and pervaded all things.

The effect of heat on various substances was the basis of early chemistry. Heating increases the thermal energy and agitation of atoms and molecules and makes them more reactive and hence liable to change their combination with other atoms and molecules. It was known that heating clay caused it to harden and pots could be made. With better knowledge of fire, bronze could be made by melting (alloying) copper with tin, and with even hotter temperatures, iron, from their respective ores. The military implications of this were obvious. Science has ever been the handmaiden of the chieftain, demanding better weaponry. In addition, various substances could be used as pigments, either to adorn the person, or the pots.

Gold has always had a special quasi-magical property, being indestructible (it doesn't rust or tarnish, nor does it dissolve in ordinary acids, unlike other metals – only being soluble in a mixture of nitric and sulphuric acids – *aqua regia*). It is in short supply, easily worked into ornaments and adornments, and currency, and is to this day regarded as the supreme token of national wealth (Gold Reserves). Gold equals power, and all power corrupts, and absolute power corrupts absolutely (Lord Acton). It not only corrupts, it actually drives people mad, as anyone who has suffered under a dictatorship knows only too well.

The study of history depends on a written record and the earliest writings with regard to the subject of chemistry (in the Western world at any rate) appear to be in Sanscrit or Arabic, where it was called al-chemy. One of the earliest classifications of chemical substances was a text called 'The Secret of Secrets' by a Persian physician called Al Razi or **Rhazes** (AD850–923). He described the properties of metals, salts, and various minerals by their solubility, their taste – sweet, sour, acid, salt – the effect of heating, and their reactions with sal ammoniac (ammonium chloride). This led to the purification of what we now call sulphuric acid (spirit of sulphur), hydrochloric (spirit of salt), and nitric acids (spirit of nitre) in the thirteenth century. Unfortunately alchemy fell into disrepute, and into the hands of quacks and charlatans with their search for the 'elixir of life' and the 'philosophers' stone', a substance which, when added to mercury, they thought would turn it into gold.

Robert **Boyle** (Robyn) (1627–1691) 'The Father of Chemistry' was a the seventh son and fourteenth child out of a total of fifteen born at Lismore Castle to the Earl and Countess of Cork (one of his elder brothers, Roger, was the first Earl of Orrery). He was sent to Eton at the age of nine, where he spent three happy years under the benign care of Mr John Harrison, the Rector of the College. After travelling in Europe, he settled at Stalbridge in Dorset, which had been given him by his father. In 1645, together with 'divers worthy persons' he was instrumental in the founding of the Royal Society, which received its Charter of Incorporation from King Charles II, on 15 July 1662.

He was a prolific writer, mostly critical of Aristotle's notions. In 1661 he wrote *The Skeptical Chemist*. He discovered a test to distinguish acids from alkalis using an 'indicator' – syrup of violets, a forerunner of litmus paper. By virtue of his birth and wealth, he had no need to seek a fortune, and hence fame (unlike Newton), in the misguided search for the philosophers' stone, and was highly critical of the ideas and practice of the alchemists.

In 1658 Robert Boyle assisted by Robert **Hooke** (1635–1703) in England built his own air pump and showed that, with a constant temperature, pressure (or 'spring' as it was then called), was inversely proportional to volume: in scientific notation, $P \times V = K$ (constant), known as Boyle's Law. Hooke in his youth wanted to be an artist and he was a competent experimental scientist as well. He was appointed Curator of Experiments at the Royal Society in 1662. In 1664 he published *Micrographia*, the first major work describing and illustrating microscopic appearances. His most famous discovery was the detailed cellular appearance of cork under the microscope.

Joseph **Black** (1728–1791) after qualifying MD in 1754, became the first professor of Chemistry at Glasgow University. He described quantitatively the reactions of acids and alkalis including 'fixed air' which we now know as carbon dioxide. He also contributed to the concept of specific heat.

In the seventeenth century, with the beginnings of the Industrial Revolution and the problems connected with mining, glass and pottery, brewing and wine making, chemists began to be taken seriously. Chemistry unfortunately suffered a setback owing to the development of the *phlogiston* theory by the German chemist Georg **Stahl** (1660–1734). The existence of this substance was postulated in order to explain chemical reactions, particularly combustion. 'It is not strictly defined and therefore fits all the explanations demanded of it,' wrote Lavoisier in 1773. 'Sometimes it has weight, sometimes not. Sometimes it passes through the pores of vessels, sometimes not. It explains at once causticity and non-causticity, transparency and opacity, colour and the absence of colour. It is a veritable Proteus, changing its form every instant.' Yet many eminent scientists of the day, Black, Priestly and Cavendish sincerely believed in its existence, and it was not until the end of the eighteenth century that Lavoisier finally drove the nail into the coffin of phlogiston.

Joseph **Priestley** (1733–1804) was the son of a cloth dresser, born at Fieldhead, near Leeds. His mother died when he was seven years old and he was brought up by a strongly Calvinist aunt. For three years he studied theology and was appointed assistant to the Presbyterian Minister at Needham Market, at £30 per annum. However it appears that his religious views were unorthodox and he became a tutor in languages at Warrington Academy. After six years at the Academy he accepted a post to take charge of the Mill Hill Chapel at Leeds.

It was while there that he performed many of his experiments, particularly with gases – *Experiments and Observations on Different Kinds of Air*, was published in 1774. Living near a brewery he had ample supplies of fixed air (CO_2) which, when dissolved in water, produced 'soda water'. For this he was awarded the Copley Medal by the Royal Society. He had a patron, and was assisted in his researches by Sir William Petty, second Earl of Shelburne, who provided him with a house and 250 guineas a year. During this time Priestley had isolated nitric oxide, nitrous oxide, ammonia, hydrochloric acid and sulphur dioxide. On 1 August 1774 he made his most famous discovery, dephlogisticated air which we now call oxygen, by focusing the Sun's rays though a large 12-inch diameter lens on to a phial containing red mercuric oxide.

It should be noted that the Swedish apothecary Karl Wilhelm **Scheele** had made a similar discovery at about the same time, as well as discovering and isolating the vegetable acids, tartaric, oxalic, benzoic, citric, prussic acid (hydrogen cyanide) and hydrofluoric acid.

Priestley moved to Birmingham in 1780 and joined the Lunar Society, which met when the Moon was full so that its members could find their way home. Other members were James Watt and Matthew Boulton (steam engines), William Withering (of digitalis fame) and John Baskerville (typefaces). Priestley's writings had led to him being called a 'dissenter', refusing to accept the authority of the Church, a free-thinker.

In 1791, with the storming of the Bastille occurring in France in 1789, an outbreak of mob violence, encouraged by members of the Established Church, took place in Birmingham, and Priestley's house was set on fire, with total destruction. He moved to Dudley, then to London. Renewed threats of violence led him to take ship to America and he settled at Northumberland, Pennsylvania. There he was offered the Professorship of Chemistry at Pennsylvania University, but in spite of the work of Lavoisier he continued to believe in the phlogiston theory.

The Hon. Henry **Cavendish** (1731–1810) was the elder son of Lord Charles Cavendish, the third son of the Second Duke of Devonshire of Chatsworth House, Derbyshire. He is known for his extraordinary accurate quantitative measurements of the composition of air and water, establishing that air was 20.833% oxygen (which he called dephlogisticated air) and 79.167% nitrogen. There was always $1/120$ part that could not be accounted for, anticipating by 100 years the discovery of argon by Lord **Rayleigh**. He determined the composition of water, proving that two parts of hydrogen (which he called inflammable air) combined with one of oxygen, giving the formula H_2O, in present notation.

He was a very shy man, immensely wealthy, with three London properties in Gower St, Soho and Clapham. He refused to have his portrait painted, the only drawing having been made surreptitiously while he was dining with Sir Joseph Banks. He also measured the Gravitational Constant (see Chapter 5). He was terrified of women and never married. When he died his estate was estimated at £1,000,000. He bequeathed it to relatives, and his Uncle, the 7th Duke of Devonshire, founded the famous Cavendish Laboratory in Cambridge, set up by James **Clerk Maxwell** in 1874.

Antoine Laurent **Lavoisier** (1743–1794), heated metallic mercury with air in a vessel in 1770. A red powder was formed, and the remaining gas could not support life, and was called azote, later renamed nitrogen. When the red powder was heated, a gas was driven off which supported life and combustion and was called oxygène – acid producer (*sauerstoff* in German) as its combination with certain non-metallic elements formed acid. At the time it was thought that all acids contained oxygen; later it became apparent that this was not the case when hydrochloric acid was discovered. Although he studied law for a time, his inclinations were towards science and he became a member of the Academy of Sciences in 1768. About the same time he took a step that was to end, 26 years later, on the scaffold. He became a member of the *Ferme Generale*, a company dedicated to the collection of taxes, corrupt and much hated, but providing a large income for its members. In 1771, aged 28, he married Marie-Anne Pierette, aged 14, only daughter of the Fermier General, Jacques Paulze. She was a skilful artist, studied under J.L. David the famous French painter and engraver, and learnt English. She was immensely helpful to her husband in his experiments. She died in 1836, aged 78, having married

Lavoisier's laboratory c.1770. Madam Lavoisier is seen seated on the right, recording details of her husband's experiments.

(unhappily) Count Rumford after her husband's death. She saw to it that Lavoisier's work and ideas endured.

In 1771 the French chemist **Guyton de Morveau** showed that metals increased in weight when burnt. This led to the abandonment of the phlogiston theory. In 1782 Guyton, Lavoisier, Berthollet and Fourcroy published *Methode de nomenclature chimique* using a new basis of nomenclature. Substances that could not be decomposed were called elements. Soon translated into English and German, it became the basis of chemistry for the next few decades.

In 1789 Lavoisier produced his famous *Traite Elem. de Chimie*, a logical summary of his findings and a system of chemical nomenclature; words of the elements, compounds and acids that survive to this day. He thought that heat was a subtle weightless fluid which he called *caloric* and in this he was wrong. He was a member of the board that introduced the *metric system*, that was subsequently universally adopted. His life ended on the scaffold. He was denounced by the chemist Fourcroy, perhaps motivated by jealousy, on account of the fact that he belonged to the Fermiers, 27 members of which were brought before the Convention and sentenced to death. Accused of being Enemies of France, all petitions for mercy were rejected.

The vice-president of the Revolutionary Tribunal, Coffinhal, when mitigating circumstances were suggested, replied *'La Republique n'a pas besion de savants, il faut que la justice suive son cours'* (The Republic has no need for scientists, justice must take its course). And the cold steel of the guillotine descended. The Place de la Concorde was awash with blood – the carotid arteries continue to pump following decapitation – the stench was so horrible that even the cattle would not go near it. However, such is the Madness of Revolution, that it was not long before Coffinhal met a similar fate.

It has been estimated that more than 40,000 people died in the bloodbath as old scores were settled. 'O Liberty', cried Mme Roland, as she mounted the scaffold, 'what crimes are committed in thy name!'

In 1808 the English chemist John **Dalton** (1766–1844) published a book summarising existing knowledge and suggesting that all matter was composed of individual *atoms* – a suggestion made previously by **Democritus** of Athens about 450BC, and who also thought that different substances were due to different arrangements of the atoms, an amazing intuition.

Dalton honoured Democritus by keeping his original word a-tome – indivisible. He defined the atom as the smallest part of a chemical element that takes part in a chemical reaction, and that what distinguishes the elements is the nature of the individual atoms, manifested by their weight, and there were as many different atoms as there were elements.

Groups of atoms are called *molecules*; if more than one kind of atom is present in a substance, it is called a molecule of a chemical *compound*. Thus water is a compound as it contains atoms of both oxygen and hydrogen. Dalton wrote a paper on the subject of colour blindness, from which he suffered, and red/green blindness is sometimes called daltonism.

Originally, the atomic weight (mass) of an element was the weight of that substance that would combine with the weight of another substance, given that hydrogen has the weight of 1.0. Then (1850) the arbitrary weight was taken to be oxygen, 16.0000, making hydrogen 1.008. Now (1960) the standard is ^{12}C (the mass of Carbon isotope 12) giving one atomic mass (hydrogen) 1.66×10^{-27}kg, sometimes called the dalton. Dalton's notation of atoms was symbolised by a circle indicating hydrogen. Oxygen was a circle with a dot in it, nitrogen a circle with a line through it. Dalton agreed that substances always combine in definite proportions, based on the work of the French chemist Joseph Louis **Proust** in 1799.

In 1811 the Italian Chemist Amedeo **Avogadro** proposed that equal volumes of gas at the same temperature and pressure contained the same number of molecules. This, the Avogadro number, is 6.16×10^{23} molecules in one gram-molecule, the molecular weight of the substance in grams.

In 1813 the Swedish chemist J. J. **Berzelius** (1779–1848) introduced a rational symbolism based on the Latin names of the elements, hydrogen became H, oxygen O, gold Au (Latin: *aurum*) Silver Ag (Latin: *argentum*) etc. and in 1828 he published a list of atomic weights.

In 1828 the German chemist Freidrich **Wohler**, a student of Berzelius, heated ammonium cyanate, an inorganic compound, and produced urea, found in urine. Berzelius thought that only living tissue could form urea.

In 1845 the German chemist **Kolbe** synthesised acetic acid. The notion of *vitalism*, that only living tissues could produce organic compounds was thus abandoned. *Organic* compounds were defined as those containing carbon, with the exception of a few simple inorganic compounds such as carbon dioxide and carbonates. The structure of organic compounds, containing many atoms of oxygen, hydrogen and nitrogen as well as carbon, defied definition until it was realised that one atom could only combine with a certain fixed number of other atoms. In 1852 the English chemist Edward **Frankland** called these ratios *valence* bonds. Thus carbon could combine with 4 other atoms, oxygen with 2, nitrogen with 3, hydrogen with 1.

In the 1830s came the development of gas lighting. Gas produced from heating coal, largely the inflammable but intensely poisonous carbon monoxide, left a residue of a black sticky substance – coal tar, which could be used as a preservative for railway sleepers. Also from coal tar many organic substances could be produced. One of these was *phenol*, which acted as an antiseptic. Another was *aniline*, which when oxidised with potassium dichromate produced the purple dye *mauve*, a process discovered by the chemist W. H. **Perkin** in 1856 at the age of eighteen. Perkin was working under the direction of the German chemist **von Hoffmann**, who had been brought over by Queen Victoria at the instigation of her husband Prince Albert to teach chemistry at the College of Science. This discovery formed the basis of the dyestuff industry. Perkin was looking for a means of synthesising quinine at the time – a classic example of serendipity. Prior to this, dyes had been produced from plants. Perkin patented his process and at the age of 23 was a world expert on dyes, and mauve became all the rage in the clothing industry – the Mauve Decade.

In 1845 the Royal College of Chemistry was set up in London, but did not receive State support until 1853.

In 1862 the German chemist Friedrich **Kekulé** von Stradonitz published a book containing illustrations of organic compounds using dashes (–) to indicate valence bonds, as suggested by the Scottish chemist Archibald Scott **Couper**. Using this system it was possible to distinguish two compounds with the same numbers of atoms, but with totally different properties. These were called *isomers*. Thus ethyl alcohol ($C_2 H_5 OH$) and dimethyl ether have the same number of atoms, but different structures, and different properties.

$$
\begin{array}{cc}
\begin{array}{c}
\text{H \ \ H} \\
\text{H} - \text{C} - \text{C} - \text{O} - \text{H} \\
\text{H \ \ H} \\
\text{Alcohol}
\end{array}
&
\begin{array}{c}
\text{H \ \ \ \ \ \ H} \\
\text{H} - \text{C} - \text{O} - \text{C} - \text{H} \\
\text{H \ \ \ \ \ \ H} \\
\text{Ether}
\end{array}
\end{array}
$$

(can also be written $CH_3 O CH_3$)

But one compound resisted formulation. That was the liquid *benzene*, which had been discovered by Faraday in 1825 and contained 6 carbon atoms and 6 hydrogen atoms. There was no way that a simple structural formula could be derived. One day, so it is said, the chemist Kekulé, riding in an omnibus, in a dreamy state imagined the carbon atoms dancing about and eventually linking up to form a ring. This was the answer. Benzene has a ring structure with double bonds linking the carbon atoms. Compounds containing benzene rings are called *aromatic*, other compounds are called *aliphatic*.

In 1884 the Swedish chemist Svante August **Arrhenius** submitted his thesis for PhD. In this, he proposed his theory of the ionic nature of atoms in solution, which would explain electrical conductivity. He suggested that, in a salt solution, sodium atoms acquire a positive charge, moving toward the negative electrode, the cathode, and are 'cations'. Chlorine atoms acquire a negative charge, move towards the positive electrode the anode, and are 'anions'. His examiners considered his ideas so absurd that they only reluctantly passed him, with the lowest grade possible. However, with the discovery of the electron in the 1890s he was vindicated and awarded the Nobel Prize for chemistry in 1906. Arrhenius also thought that the origin of life was extraterrestrial.

In 1869, modified in 1871, The Russian scientist Dmitri Ivanovitsch Mendeleeff (1834–1907) published his *Periodic Table* (see Appendix) relating atomic weights with properties. This was based on an idea by the English chemist J.A.R. **Newlands** that, if the elements are arranged in order of atomic weights, every 8th element repeats the same properties, the 'law of octaves'. Mendeleeff's table predicted the properties of as yet undiscovered elements and was vindicated when *gallium* was discovered in 1875, *scandium* in 1879 and *germanium* in 1886.

Mendeleeff was the 14th child of his parents, born in Tobolsk, Siberia – a place of banishment for political exiles. He was much encouraged by his extremely intelligent and industrious mother, Marya Dmitrievna, who ran a paper and glass factory when her husband became blind. She was self-educated as it was not considered proper for girls to have an education, so she obtained her knowledge from her older brother. The factory was destroyed by fire and the family moved to St Petersburg, and, with the help of one of her late husband's friends, Marya managed to obtain a place for young Dmitri at the Physico-Mathematical Faculty of the Central Pedagogic Institute, where he developed his interest in science. He recorded his mother's dying words – 'Refrain from illusions, insist on work, not on words. Patiently search divine and scientific truth'. Apart from his scientific distinction, he was noted for his prolific hairstyle. He only had his hair cut once a year, in spring.

In 1890 he was elected a Foreign Member of the Royal Society, and in 1905 received the Copley Medal, yet he never became a member of the Imperial Academy of Sciences of St Petersburg, perhaps an illustration of the saying that one can never be a prophet in one'sown country One of his more interesting beliefs was that hydrocarbons are formed, not by decomposing organic remains, but by the action of water on metallic carbides deep in the Earth.

At the beginning of the nineteenth century quantitative study of chemical reactions led to the realization that reactions could be speeded up. Berzelius introduced the word *catalyst* for substances that achieved this, especially finally divided platinum that would facilitate the combination of oxygen and hydrogen to form water, at low temperatures. Acids facilitate the breakdown of starch to sugar. Vanadium pentoxide facilitates the conversion of sulphur dioxide to sulphur trioxide in the manufacture of sulphuric acid. The mechanism appears to be that the excess electrons in the valence bonds of metals react with the atoms of the substances in question making them in turn reactive. Metals like platinum are used because in their natural state they are non-reactive, like gold, which can only be dissolved in *aqua regia*, a mixture of sulphuric and nitric acids. They have to be in fine suspension, in order to present a large surface area, and emerge unchanged after the reaction. Platinum, palladium and rhodium are used in a ceramic matrix, in *catalytic converters* of cars to oxidise the poisonous residues of internal combustion, carbon monoxide, hydrocarbons and oxides of nitrogen. Lead-free petrol must be used since lead would inactivate or poison the platinum.

The earliest example of catalysis was the use of *yeast* (saccharomyces – a single celled fungus) in the baking of bread. The ancient Egyptians found that by adding yeast in bread-making it could be made to 'rise' by virtue of gas bubbles (carbon dioxide) that were produced, and thereby made more palatable. Yeast is used in the process of fermentation, in which the sugars of fruit juices are turned into alcohol. The cells of yeast had been seen under the microscope to be dividing, and therefore living. The German chemist Eduard **Buchner** in 1897 discovered that ground up yeast cells could cause fermentation, and in 1898 the German physiologist Wilhelm **Kühne** coined the word '*enzyme*' – 'in yeast', to name the factor that was responsible for the chemical transformation, and the distinction between life and non-life became blurred.

Enzymes are organic catalysts, in fact protein catalysts, and their activity is abolished by denaturing the protein, by heating for instance. Some 2000 enzymes have now been identified and

200 crystallised. They are very efficient, active in tiny amounts, and very specific. They are also very sensitive to poisons, particularly metals, and the heavier the metal, the more poisonous. The man-made element plutonium, Atomic Number 94, besides being radioactive, half-life of its principal isotope 239 – 24,000 years, is extremely toxic. Metals react with the thiol (SH) groups of enzymes, inactivating them. The gas carbon monoxide is poisonous by virtue of its affinity for the blood pigment haem, which, in association with the protein globin, is responsible for the transport of oxygen to the tissues.

Haem has an iron atom in the centre of 4 pyrrole rings. In the tissues *oxyhaemoglobin*, which is red, gives up its oxygen and becomes reduced haemoglobin, which is purple (cyanosis). Carbon monoxide displaces oxygen from the haemoglobin molecule forming a stable compound carboxyhaemoglobin, which is pink. People who have died of carbon monoxide poisoning are pink.

The word *protein*, from a Greek word meaning of first importance, was coined by the Dutch chemist G.J. **Mulder** in 1839, after a suggestion by Berzelius. Proteins were found to be made up of amino-acids. The first amino acid, *glycine*, was identified in 1820 by the French chemist Henri **Braconnot** by heating gelatin within an acid solution, and found to contain nitrogen. The structural formula was later worked out to be:

$$NH_2 - C^*H_2 - COOH.$$

The NH_2 group is an amine, and the COOH, carboxyl, group is acidic, hence the name amino-acid. Different side chains are attached at C^*, giving different properties to the resulting amino-acids. Twenty different amino acids have now been identified. Proteins are made of amino-acids, in varying numbers and of varying types. A molecule of albumen (white of egg) with a molecular weight of 80,000, contains 500 amino acids. The amino-acids are linked by *peptide* chains, the NH_2 group of one amino-acid joining the COOH group of another, and proteins are polypeptides.

This was first demonstrated by the German chemist Emil **Fischer** in 1901, who condensed two glycine molecules together with the elimination of a molecule of water. He called the linkage peptide, from a Greek word meaning digest. The complete structure of albumen, the first protein molecule to be analysed, was worked out by the British biochemists Frederick **Sanger** and Hans **Tuppy** in 1953.

There are two basic types of protein, fibrous, such as collagen and keratin, which have a long alpha-helix structure and are insoluble in water, and globular proteins, such as the plasma proteins albumen and globulin, which are spherical and highly soluble in water.

The amino acid glycine is symmetrical, but amino-acids with longer side chains are asymmetrical about the carbon atom marked *, when one of the hydrogen atoms is substituted by a longer side chain. This gives rise to two different *isomers*, molecules with the same number of atoms and hence chemical formula, but different structures and hence different properties. One is the ability to rotate the plane of polarised light, called optical activity (see Chapter 5).

In 1844 Louis **Pasteur** (aged 22) studied this using salts of tartaric acid, derived from fermented grape juice. Under the microscope, he found that there were two distinct crystal forms, and painstakingly he separated the left hand ones from the right hand ones. When these were converted into acids and dissolved in water he found that one sort rotated the plane of polarised light to the left and the other to the right. The German chemist Emil **Fischer**, using glyceraldehyde, named the left hand forms L(+) laevo rotatory (anti-clockwise) and the right hand forms D(-) dextrotatory (clockwise). Nearly all the amino acids are of the L form while nearly all the sugars are the D form, hence Dextrose, the D form of glucose.

It is interesting to note that living forms introduce handedness into the cosmic scheme of things. Laterality does not seem to appear in the purely physical world except possibly some fundamental particles. It makes no difference whether stars or planets rotate clockwise or anti clockwise. The concept of Left and

Right is a comparatively recent one, and impossible to define without a reference point, the equally arbitrary North and South. The language of the Australian aborigines apparently has no words for left and right. Only with the introduction of navigation did it become important.

While chemical synthesis has produced many useful products, such as acrylic and nylon for clothes, polythene and perspex, antibiotics and other medicinal remedies, there is a downside in that many products, particularly herbicides and insecticides which are extremely toxic.

DDT (dichloro diphenyl trichlorethane) was discovered to be a powerful insecticide in 1939 by the Swiss chemist H. **Muller**, and was very effective against fleas, mosquitoes and lice, the carriers of many diseases. However resistance soon develops. It is fat soluble and accumulates in the bodies of birds and fishes that eat insects, with disastrous effects, causing very weak shells in birds' eggs. In 1972 its use was restricted in the USA.

It is possible that Alzheimer's disease and similar conditions of brain failure are due to poisoning, perhaps by heavy metals, which are extremely toxic to living tissues, or by insecticide organophosphates (malathion, chlorovos) which block nerve conduction.

Many synthetic chemicals are toxic in extremely low dose and accumulate because they do not enter any metabolic pathways. They have been implicated in the sex changes of some fishes and molluscs, and lowering the age of puberty. Lindane, which has now been banned, is toxic to fishes in a concentration of one part per million.

The chemical industry now amounts to £250 billion a year worldwide, and an estimated 13,000 chemicals are now produced, of which only 14% have any safety data publicly available. Legislation is now proposed to improve the situation.

It is therefore incumbent on Governments to monitor and regulate them very closely.

CHAPTER FIVE

PHYSICS

'Physics is the only Science –
Everything else is stamp collecting.'   Rutherford

The trouble with specialisation is that the specialist thinks his discipline is the only one worth studying. After a while he thinks it is the only one that exists. This attitude is not, in the long run, helpful.

Classical physics has four disciplines – mechanics, heat, optics, and electromagnetism.

MECHANICS

A branch of mathematics dealing with the motion of bodies, and the forces which control bodies. **Dynamics** is concerned with moving bodies, **statics** with bodies at rest.

Galileo experimented with the motion of falling bodies and concluded that acceleration was constant and independent of the mass of the falling body. Also that a projectile had a parabolic trajectory as a consequence of the two forces acting upon it, one horizontal as a consequence of its forward motion, the other vertical as a consequence of the force of gravity.

Isaac **Newton** expressed the matter mathematically with his Three Laws of Motion expounded in his **Principia Mathematica** published in 1687, written in Latin. His subsequent work **Opticks**, published in 1704, was in English, suggesting that English rather than Latin was becoming the *lingua franca* of science.

1. **Force** is that which causes a change of velocity of an object. Force has magnitude and direction. **Centrifugal force** due to rotation is v^2/r, where r is the distance between the object and

the centre of rotation and v the angular velocity. ***Coriolis force*** (G.G. **Coriolis** – French physicist 1792–1843) - F = 2ø sin Uv, where F is the magnitude of the horizontal component, ø is the angular velocity of the Earth, U is the latitude, v is the horizontal velocity of the moving body.

The Coriolis force is a rotatory force whose axis of rotation is perpendicular to the axis of rotation of a revolving body. It causes water draining down a hole to rotate clockwise in the northern hemisphere and anticlockwise in the southern hemisphere. It is responsible for weather systems, particularly hurricanes and may be responsible for the Great Red Spot on the planet Jupiter, as well as the orientation of the planets in the ecliptic in the equatorial plane of the Sun. It is also responsible for the ocean currents such as the Gulf Stream and the Humboldt current.

2. ***Inertia.*** A body will continue at rest or to move in a straight line unless a force acts upon it (Newton's First Law). It then has ***momentum*** which is expressed as mv where m is the mass of the body and v is its velocity. ***Angular momentum*** of a rotating body is expressed as mvr where r is the distance of the body from its centre of rotation. (Hence an ice skater will spin faster when his or her arms are moved inwards, thus conserving momentum – the velocity increases as the radius of the mass decreases).

3. ***Acceleration.*** A force f will be required to produce an acceleration a of a mass m. $f = m\ a$. (Newton's Second Law of Motion).

4. For every action there is an equal and opposite reaction. (Newton's Third Law of Motion). This is the principle of rocket propulsion.

From these laws Newton concluded that the gravitational force between any two bodies was directly proportional to the masses of the bodies and inversely proportional to the square of distances between the centres of the bodies. It was the genius of

Newton that he realised that the force causing the proverbial apple to fall on to his head in his garden in Woolsthorpe, Lincolnshire, whither he had gone in 1665 to escape the Great Plague, was the same as that which kept the Moon and planets in their orbits. This is Newton's Law of Universal Gravitation, and can be expressed mathematically:

$$f = \frac{m_1 \, m_2}{d^2} \times G, \quad \text{where G is the Gravitational}$$

Constant m_1 and m_2 are the masses whose centres of gravity are d apart. The value of G was determined experimentally by Henry Cavendish in 1798 by measuring the torsional force needed to balance the gravitational attraction between two suspended large masses.

Refined measurements show it to be now 6.6726×10^{-8} dyne centimetre squared per gram squared. From this the mass of the Earth can be calculated. It is 6.585×10^{21} tons or 5.976×10^{24} kilograms. Knowing the volume of the Earth, its density can be calculated and is 5.518 grams per cubic centimetre (the density of water is 1).

The **newton** is the unit of force that is required to accelerate one kilogram by one metre per second per second and is equal to 105 dynes. The **dyne** is the CGS unit of force and is the force required to accelerate one gram by one centimetre per second per second.

Work is force times distance. The CGS unit of work is the **erg** which is the work done by a force of one dyne acting over one centimetre. The practical unit of work is the **joule** which is a force of one newton acting over a distance of one metre. It is equal to 10^7 ergs.

Power is the rate of doing work. $P = w/t$, where w is the amount of work done in time t. The SI unit of power is the **watt**. It is the power dissipated when one joule is expended in one second (its ratification was delayed for seven years until 1889 owing to the difficulty the French have in pronouncing the letter w).

There are 746 watts in one horse-power.

Energy is the capacity to do work. It has magnitude only. *Potential energy* is stored energy due to position, and is the amount of work required to put an object into its original position. E = m h g where m is the mass of the object, h is the height to which it is raised, and g is the acceleration due to gravity (32 feet or 9.8 metres per second per second.)

Kinetic energy is the energy of motion of a moving body and $E = \frac{1}{2}mv^2$, where v is the velocity of the body and m its mass.

Weight is mass times gravity (Earth's gravity = 1). The SI unit of mass is the kilogram. The standard prototype of mass is a platinum/iridium cylinder preserved at the International Bureau of Weights and measures at Sevres, near Paris and is unique in that it is the only one of the seven basic SI units that is man-made. Copy No.18 is at the National Physical Laboratory, England, and copy No.20 in the USA.

Pressure is the force acting at right angles to unit area. The SI unit of pressure is the *pascal*, a force of one newton per square metre.

The *bar* is a unit of atmospheric pressure, and is 105 pascals. Sea level atmospheric pressure averages 760mm of mercury. One *torr* is a pressure equal to one millimetre of mercury. Blood pressure is still measured in millimetres of mercury; air pressure in pounds per square inch, or millibars. One Standard Atmosphere is 1013 millibars, or 14.7 pounds per square inch.

Density or *Specific Gravity* is weight per unit volume, with reference to water = 1.

One of the great principles of physics is the Law of Conservation of Energy, which states that energy can neither be created nor destroyed, only transformed into different forms. Thermal energy can be transformed into mechanical energy which can be transformed into electrical energy. Atomic physics however appears to defy this law, as the transformation of matter into energy and its reciprocal is manifest in nuclear reactions, expressed in Einstein's famous equation, $E = mc^2$, where m is mass and c is the velocity of light. The radiation from one gram of radium will boil one gram of water in one minute without any change in the mass of the radium. This unit is the *curie*. (now defined as 37×10^9 disintegrations per second).

Momentum must be conserved as must angular momentum.

HEAT

The nature of *heat* was disputed for many years. Lavoisier and others thought it to be a subtle weightless fluid called *caloric*. It is now known to be a form of *energy*, manifested by thermal agitation of atoms and molecules, which results in several *phases* or *states* of matter.

Solids, have shape and volume; atoms and molecules are held in a rigid structure, often crystalline, with little agitation.

Liquids have volume but no shape and atoms and molecules move in larger groups, with less cohesion than solids. This was first demonstrated by the English Botanist Robert **Brown** in 1827, who showed that particles of pollen, with an average diameter of 50μ, when suspended in water, moved irregularly under the microscope – *Brownian Motion*. Some solids become gases without the intervening liquid state. This is called *sublimation*. Carbon dioxide is a good example of this.

Viscosity is the tendency of a fluid to resist a shearing force due to its internal friction. Liquid helium Π is a liquid without viscosity, penetrates glass, defies gravity, can only be solidified under immense pressure.

Gases have neither shape nor volume, particles have minimal cohesion and move freely.

A fourth state of matter is *plasma*, so hot that atoms are stripped of their electrons. Most of the matter in the universe exists in the form of plasma.

There is a fifth phase, that of the *liquid crystal* discovered in 1888 by the Austrian botanist Friedrich **Reinitzer**. It was found that certain organic molecules, such as myelin (the fatty compound that forms the insulating sheaths of nerve fibres), p-azoxyanisole (PAA), cholesterol benzoate and 4-n-hexyl - 4 - cyanobiphenyl, when heated from the solid state undergo a transition before becoming liquid, that involves a very thin (molecular) layer of crystals that have remarkable properties. These crystals exist as rods or flat plates that change colour with temperature, and orient themselves when put in an electric field. LCDs (liquid crystal displays) are now extensively used in digital watches and video display units as they use very little current to achieve their desired objective.

Colloids are another form of matter, in which particles between 10μ and 1 nanometre are held in suspension, as opposed to solution. The suspended particles are called the dispersed phase, the medium, the dispersion medium.

An *aerosol* is a colloidal dispersion of either a liquid or a solid in a gas. An *emulsion* is a dispersion of a liquid in a liquid. A *sol* is a suspension of a solid in a liquid. A *gel* is a sol in which the particles are suspended in an organised medium which gives it rigidity.

Electrophoresis is a technique in which the movement of particles in suspension in a fluid when under the influence of an electric field is observed and measured.

Specific Heat is the quantity of heat required to raise the temperature of a substance through one degree Celsius, given water as one.

Heat can be transferred in three ways:

1. Conduction, in which two bodies are in direct contact.
2. Convection, in which heat is transferred by means of a liquid medium such as water, as in domestic heating systems, or a gas, such as air in domestic hot air systems, or carbon dioxide as in AGC (advanced gas cooled) nuclear reactors.
3. Radiation – infra-red electromagnetic radiation with wavelengths about 1μ–100μ. Microwave ovens work at about 12.3μ.

If a liquid is allowed to evaporate rapidly it gains energy, extracting heat from its surroundings, which then cools. This is the principle of *refrigeration* (as well as sweating). If air is compressed and cooled to ordinary temperatures and then allowed to expand, it becomes quite cold. If this cold air is further compressed and then allowed to expand, the air will eventually liquefy, and then can be separated into its constituents, oxygen, nitrogen, argon, etc. At atmospheric pressure, oxygen liquefies at -183°C and freezes at -218°C, and nitrogen liquefies at -195°C and freezes at -210°C.

Helium liquefies at 4.2K (-269°C) and solidifies at -272 °C under 25 atmospheres pressure (absolute zero, 0K is -273.16°C). It cannot freeze under normal pressure. Liquid helium is a **superconductor**, 1000 times better than copper. At 2.19K (-270° C) it becomes Helium 2, and superfluid, creeping up the side of a glass container and penetrating holes so tiny that gases will not flow through. It is used in nuclear magnetic resonance scanners to keep the electro-magnets in their superconducting state. Helium gas is used in balloons, as it is lighter than air and non-inflammable. It is obtained from natural gas wells, where it amounts to about 0.4% of the volume, most of it being methane.

Cryogenics is the study of materials at temperatures below -183C°

In 1798 the American adventurer Sir Benjamin Thompson (Count **Rumford** 1753–1814) while boring cannon in Bavaria found inexhaustible amounts of heat being generated and suggested it was purely due to mechanical friction and was a form of energy and presented a paper to the Royal Society to this effect.

He was a man of tremendous energy. Philosopher, philanderer, philanthropist, consummate politician, economical with the truth, social climber. He had one legitimate and at least two illegitimate children and one of his mistresses was Lady Palmerston (Mary Mee). Her husband, Lord Palmerston (the 2nd Viscount, that is, father of the 3rd who became Prime Minister in 1855) had Emma Hamilton, who in turn had Horatio Nelson. He later married Mme Lavoisier, widow of the famous French scientist, but it was not a happy union.

He went to England and bought a commission for £4,500 and embarked for America to fight on the side of the English. His ship was blown off course and did not arrive until several weeks after Cornwallis had surrendered at Yorktown and did not see much military action. His troops were by all accounts an ill-disciplined rabble. On his return to England he recounted his 'triumphs' and was knighted by George III.

He invented enclosed ovens and fireplaces, and an improved coffee pot. His researches in heat loss suggested wearing cotton in summer, wool in winter. He got himself appointed ADC and later Chamberlain to Carl Theodore, the Duke of Bavaria and Elector Palatine. He set up an Academy of Science in Munich and improved the military and in 1792 was appointed Graf von Rumford of the Holy Roman Empire. He designed the Standard Candle, the unit of illumination.

Always concerned to improve the lot of the poor, together with the philanthropist Sir Thomas **Bernard**, and Sir Joseph **Banks**, the then President of the Royal Society, Rumford wanted to set up an Institution as a training ground for mechanics and artisans, particularly to demonstrate Rumford's improved cooking and heating methods. Banks thought it should be for a series of lectures to enlighten the leisured classes.

The Institution was set up in March 1799, the house of a Mr Mellish, 21 Albemarle Street, London W1, having been bought for the purpose. There were 38 subscribers, and 9 managers were elected. By June 1799, George III had become a patron and the *Institution* could call itself *Royal*. The first public lecture was held on 4 March 1800, in a theatre (based on Anderson's Institution in Glasgow and designed by a young architect Thomas Webster,) and was given by Professor Garnett, a widower, and lectures were held 6 days a week, twice a day. Count Volta's discovery of the electric battery was soon demonstrated.

Rumford fell out with Garnett over the syllabus of the lectures, Rumford insisting on his full supervision. Garnett resigned after the Institution refused to increase his salary and Humphry **Davy**, an assistant lecturer in chemistry, was appointed in his place. Garnett never recovered from the shock of his constructive dismissal, and he died the following year leaving his children destitute and debt ridden.

Davy was a poet and storyteller, as well as being a scientific genius. He demonstrated the effect of nitrous oxide, 'laughing gas'. He also discovered the electrolytic method of isolating metals, sodium and potassium (see Chapter 4).

Thomas **Young**, famous for demonstrating the wave nature of light, as well as deciphering the Rosetta Stone (translating Egyptian heiroglyphics), and proving 'Young's Modulus' relating the stress to the strain of a body, was also appointed a lecturer.

So popular were Davy's lectures that Albemarle Street became congested with the carriages of the gentry, and had to be made a one-way street, the first in London.

Rumford went to Munich in 1801, no doubt to check up on his pension, and thence to Paris, where he met, and was impressed by, Napoleon. He also met Pierre Simon Laplace, the famous mathematician (and bedded his wife). He also met Lagrange and the wealthy Mme Lavoisier (whose husband had perished under the Guillotine in 1794), being overwhelmed by these Parisian ladies describing them as 'most exceeding kind and obliging'. He entered into a disastrous marriage with Mme Lavoisier in 1805 and they separated in 1809. He died of a 'nervous fever' on 21 August 1814, and was buried at Auteuil.

Count Rumford had been born in 1753 in modest circumstances on a farm at Woburn, Massachusetts, about 15 miles from the prosperous port of Salem. He had obtained his first job as a teacher at the age of 19 at Concord/Rumford, near Woburn, and derived his title from that. He married a local girl, a widow and heiress aged 33 at the time, and had one legitimate daughter, Sarah, who later assumed the title Countess Rumford.

Humphry **Davy** used a mechanical device to melt two pieces of ice by rubbing them together, and it became clear that heat was a form of energy and was not a physical substance. It was the English physicist James Prescott **Joule** (1818–1889) who put the nature of heat on a scientific basis in 1840 by accurately measuring the quantity of electrical energy necessary to heat a given amount of water, and later determined the mechanical equivalent of heat. Joule's father owned a large brewery at Oldham, near Manchester, but James spent his time on scientific research. Being a brewer he had great difficulty in getting his results published – academic elitism is nothing new.

In 1847 Heinrich von **Helmholtz** proposed the Law of Conservation of Energy, that energy can neither be created nor destroyed, only be transformed from one form into another. This is the First Law of *Thermodynamics* (French physicist Sadi **Carnot** is considered the founder of the science of thermodynamics).

The capacity of any system to perform work is its *free energy*. The portion of the energy that is not available for work is its *entropy*, a term first used in 1850 by the German physicist **Clausius**. He pointed out that in any energy flow, there is always some loss, and that therefore the entropy of any system must increase. This is the Second Law of Thermodynamics. Its ultimate consequence is the cooling of the Universe.

Temperature is the measure of the average kinetic energy of the molecules of a system. Quantitative measurements of temperature were first attempted by Galileo in 1603, using the expansion of air in an inverted tube over water. The trouble was that it varied with the air pressure. Water and alcohol were used in sealed tubes but the French savant **Amonton** used mercury. In 1714 the German physicist **Fahrenheit** placed a scale alongside the column of mercury. He put zero as the lowest temperature he could obtain using a mixture of ice and salt, the freezing point of water at 32, the boiling point at 212, giving a range of 180 degrees through which water remained liquid, equivalent to the 180 degrees of a semicircle. Body temperature came out at 98.4 degrees.

In 1742 the Swedish astronomer Anders **Celsius** put the freezing point of water at 100, and the boiling point at 0 degrees. His compatriot, the Swedish botanist **Linnaeus**, inverted this scale so that the freezing point was 0 and the boiling point 100. Body temperature became 37 degrees. This is the centigrade scale, one hundred steps. In 1948 the scientific community adopted this scale attributed to Celsius as being the most convenient.

In 1787 the French physicist Jacques **Charles** showed that the volume of a gas was proportionate to its temperature, at constant pressure, and that it decreased by a fraction of $1/273$ for each degree of cooling at constant pressure. This is *Charles' Law*. Therefore it should shrink to zero at -273°. It will of course liquefy before that and liquids do not contract like gases. This difficulty was overcome by the suggestion of William **Thomson**, later Lord **Kelvin**, that although its volume could not disappear, its free energy could, and that therefore there could not be a lower temperature than -273°, called absolute zero, now known as kelvin. Modern measurements estimate absolute zero at about -273.16°C, 0 K.

Heat is the kinetic energy of all the molecules of a system. A common measure of heat is the *calorie*, defined as the amount of heat required to raise the temperature of one gram of water through one centigrade degree (the kilocalorie, 1000 calories, is often used to measure food energy).

In 1948 the International Conference on Weights and Measures adopted the *joule* as the unit of heat. One calorie equals 4.184 Joules. One joule equals 2.78×10^{-7} kilowatt hours. One KwH equals 3.6×10^6 joules. A joule is a watt-second.

Additional amounts of energy in the form of heat are necessary to break the cohesive bonds and turn a solid into a liquid. This is known as the *latent heat of fusion* and in the case of ice/water is 79.6 calories per gram, involving a contraction of 0.9%, which is unusual as most solids expand when they melt. This is the reason an iceberg will float on water – nine-tenths is submerged.

Further amounts of heat are required to convert a liquid to a gas. This is known as the *latent heat of vaporisation* and in the case of water/steam amounts to 538 calories per gram, involving an expansion of 1,700 times.

Specific heat is the quantity of heat required to raise the temperature of a substance through one degree Celsius, given water as one.

Gas Laws – It had been known for years that a pump at the top of a well could not raise water more than 33 feet. In 1644 Galileo's students **Torricelli** and **Viviani** filled a yard (metre) long tube of mercury and inverted it over a bowl of mercury. The level of mercury fell to about 30 inches (760cm) above the dish, producing a vacuum above. This was explained by assuming that the column of mercury was sustained by the weight of air above it, and this was found to vary with the weather and hence was a *barometer*.

In 1648 the French mathematician Blaise **Pascal** sent his brother-in law up a mountain with a barometer to demonstrate the fall in pressure with the altitude, thereby introducing the first altimeter. In 1662 Englishman Robert **Boyle**, showed that the pressure of a gas varies inversely with its volume, at a constant temperature: P x V = K (constant) – Boyle's Law). Boyle, also a pupil of Galileo, was one of the founder members of the Royal Society for Improving Natural Knowledge, which received its charter from Charles II in 1663.

Combining Charles' Law with Boyles, gives PV/T = constant.

OPTICS

And God said 'let there be light.' And there was light.

Genesis 1:v3

Amazingly perceptive, as modern cosmology maintains that, following the Big Bang, the moment of Creation, 'decoupling' of the universe occurred when the density of the Universe had fallen sufficiently low to permit the emergence of photons of light, when the universe became flooded with light. Be that as it may, there are certain phenomena associated with the generation, transmission and perception of light

1. Reflection – The angle of incidence is equal to the angle of reflection from a plane (flat) surface. The reflected ray, the incident ray, and the **normal** (an imaginary line at right angles to the surface of the mirror, or other reflecting surface) all lie in one plane. For a spherically curved reflecting surface, the principal focus lies halfway between the centre of curvature and the surface of the mirror.

2. Refraction – A ray of light entering a medium that is denser than air will be refracted (bent) towards the normal. The extent of this bending is the **refractive index** of the denser medium. The sine of the angle of incidence divided by the sine of the angle of refraction (with reference to the normal) is the refractive index. Refraction is due to slowing of the rays of light as they travel through a denser medium. If the velocity of light in a vacuum is taken as 1.00000, the refractive index of air is

1.0003, the refractive index of glass is 1.5-1.6, of water it is 1.33, of diamond 2.4. If a ray of light is passing from a medium with a high refractive index to one with a lower refractive index, such as water to air, there will be a *critical angle* beyond which total internal reflection will occur. With water/air it is 46 degrees. A fish, therefore will see a circle of light above, reaching to the horizon.

Snell's Law (Willebrord Snell, Dutch astronomer, 1591–1626) states that the sine of the angle of incidence divided by the sine of the angle of refraction is proportional to the reduction in velocity of a light ray travelling from one medium to another, when the latter medium is denser than the former:

$$v_1/v_2 = \sin i/\sin r = \text{refractive index (see above).}$$

If a ray of light is passing from a dense medium (glass) into a less dense medium (air) and the angle of incidence (the angle between the ray and the 'normal' which is at right angles to the surface) is much greater the 90 degrees, the ray cannot escape and total internal reflection occurs. This is the principle underlying *fibre-optic* transmission. In a fibre-optic cable, a core of 0.1 millimetre or less of silica glass is coated with a layer of cladding glass with a slightly lower refractive index, 0.1-0.3mm thick.

3. Diffraction – This is the bending or spreading of rays when they pass through a slit or aperture or round the edge of a structure. When the width of the slit approaches the wavelength of light, light and dark bands appear due to interference. This was first shown by Thomas Young and demonstrated the wave theory of light. The coloured lights that can be seen when a CD is slanted are due to the 'pits' in the track of the CD being about 400 nanometres in diameter, close to the wavelength of yellow light.

4. Polarisation – If a beam of light is shone through a crystal of Iceland spar, a transparent form of the mineral calcite which is made of calcium carbonate, the light emerges in a coherent

form, all the waves undulating in a definite plane. A development of this is the Nicol prism, invented in 1829 by the Scottish physicist William **Nicol**. If two Nicol prisms are set at right angles – crossed Nicols, all the light is cut out and this provides a sensitive detector of optical activity if a test solution is placed between them. Again, this is evidence of the wave properties of light. Nicol prisms have been supplanted by *polaroid*, made up of aligned crystals of a complex of quinine sulphate and iodine, embedded in nitrocellulose, invented in 1932 by the American scientist Edwin **Land**. Many substances show optical activity, such as quartz; and biological material such as tartaric acid, amino acids and sugars.

Electromagnetism

The word electron is derived from the Greek word for amber, a fossil tree resin. The Greek philosopher **Thales**, about 400BC, had found that when amber was rubbed with fur, it acquired the property of attracting feathers and fluff.

William **Gilbert** (1544–1603) court physician to Queen Elizabeth I suggested that this property should be called electricity. Gilbert also found that glass had a similar property, but when a glass rod touched an amber rod both lost their properties. Two amber rods repelled each other, as did two glass rods, but an amber rod attracted a glass rod. This fascinated the American printer, philosopher and statesman Benjamin **Franklin** (1706–1790) who suggested there were two kinds of electricity, positive and negative – a remarkably astute speculation. It is possible that he was led to this by the work of the French philosopher Rene **Descartes** (1596–1650). He thought that nature was essentially dualistic, everything had an opposite – the symmetry of Nature. Thus on/off (binary arithmetic), up/down, in/out, positive/negative, electron/positron, left/right, east/west, north pole/south pole (of magnets and globes), male/female, body/soul (the soul can be considered that part of the individual that is not the body), yin/yang. Everything, that is, except the force of gravity, which appears to have no opposite. Perhaps Descartes also influenced Newton, whose Third Law of Motion states that for every action there is an equal and opposite reaction. He also used the algebraic symbols x and y to represent unknown numbers, and similarly coordinates used in graphs are known as cartesian.

It was found that electric charges could be stored on conducting surfaces (inner and outer) of glass jars (Leyden Jar – invented in 1745 by the German Ewald George von **Kleist** and used at the University of Leyden in Holland). When the surfaces were joined with a copper wire which conducted electricity, a spark appeared. Franklin thought that lightning was an electrical phenomenon and in 1752 conducted his celebrated experiment during a thunderstorm using a kite with a key at the lower end of the string, but with an insulating piece of string to hold it. (some say he made his son hold the string). At any rate he proved that lightning was indeed an electrical discharge and suggested that tall buildings should be equipped with lightning conductors. He was lucky, as several people have been electrocuted trying to repeat this experiment. He was made FRS and given the Copley Medal by the Royal Society in 1753.

In 1785 the French physicist Charles Augustin de **Coulomb** showed that the attraction between charged objects varied as the square of the distance between them, similar to the force of gravity. In honour of this, the *coulomb* has been named after him. It is a unit of charge, one ampere flowing for one second.

In 1791, the Italian anatomist Luigi **Galvani** discovered that a frog's muscle would contract when the nerve supplying it was touched by two different metals.

In 1800 the Italian physicist Alessandro **Volta** experimented with different metals, eventually ending up with zinc and silver discs separated by cardboard soaked in a salt solution. This was the first electric battery, from which a continuous current of electricity could be obtained. In his honour, the *volt* has been chosen as the unit of electric potential.

In 1807, Humphry Davy using electric current from batteries to prepare metals from solution, isolated sodium, potassium, magnesium, calcium, strontium, and barium. He was a poet and a great showman and was famous for his lectures at the Royal

Institution and for inventing the miners' safety lamp, in which the naked flame was surrounded by a gauze metal mesh, preventing explosions in coal mines due to methane, the dreaded fire-damp. He also demonstrated the effect of inhaling nitrous oxide N_2O, laughing gas, which no doubt had his audience in hysterics. This gas is still used as a light anaesthetic – gas and air, nitrous oxide mixed with oxygen, is used in midwifery. The Swedish chemist J. J. Berzelius visited Davy in London and wryly commented 'a man of science would be honoured by the world until it was discovered that he unsuccessfully sought distinction in Society, and then he would become a laughing stock.' Davy went about his travels abroad.

Michael **Faraday** (1791–1867) his assistant, went on to work out the general rules of electrolysis which led, fifty years later, to Arrhenius' theory of ionic dissociation. Faraday was the son of a poor blacksmith and had a rudimentary education. At the age of 14 he had a 7 year apprenticeship with a bookbinder. A useful trade for one who had an avid desire for knowledge – one of the books he had to bind was the *Encyclopaedia Britannica*. He attended Davy's lectures at the Royal Institution. He copied out Davy's lectures and presented these, beautifully bound, to the great man. Davy advised him to stick to bookbinding. Faraday expressed this more elegantly 'he advised me not to give up the prospects I had before me... Science was a harsh mistress... and poorly rewarded...'.

One day in 1812, while attempting an experiment with nitrogen chloride at the Royal Institution, an explosion temporarily blinded Davy and he asked Faraday to be his assistant. A permanent position arose the next year when two of the Institution's assistants were involved in a fight and one of them was sacked. On 1 March 1814, Faraday was appointed laboratory assistant. He accompanied Davy on an 18-month tour of Europe and became acquainted with the learned and famous, Cuvier, Gay-Lussac, Volta, and with their ideas, and learnt to speak French. All the time, England was at war with France (Napoleonic Wars) but this did not impede the visitors. War in those days was a more gentlemanly occupation. Faraday's position was not altogether happy – Lady Davy was not an easy person, had difficulty in retaining servants, and Faraday was frequently called upon to remedy the deficiency.

In 1820 the Danish physicist Hans Christian **Oersted** showed that a wire carrying an electric current would cause a deflection of a compass needle at right angles to the direction to the flow of current, suggesting that an electric current set up a magnetic field. Faraday made use of this by constructing an electric motor where a wire through which an electric current was passing rotated around the pole of a magnet. It is reported that the visiting Prime Minister, Robert Peel, on seeing the device, said 'What on earth is the use of that Mr Faraday?'. Faraday replied, lightly, but with amazing prescience 'I know not, but I wager that one day your Government will tax it.' But 160 years was to elapse before Faraday's prediction became true, when Value Added Tax was imposed on domestic electric bills in the UK in 1993, a tax that falls disproportionately heavily on the lower income groups.

Soon after this, the French physicist Andre Marie **Ampere** showed that two parallel wires carrying electric currents in the same direction would attract each other, while if flowing in the opposite direction repelled each other. He also showed that a coil of wire through which an electric current was passing acted as a bar magnet. The *ampere* is the unit of electric current. It was originally defined in terms of electrolysis, as the current which would deposit 1.118×10^{-3} grams of silver per second from a solution of silver nitrate. It is now defined in terms of the force between two parallel wires carrying an electric current.

In 1831 Faraday performed an experiment that was to change the course of history. Arguing that if a current of electricity could influence a magnet, perhaps a magnet could generate a current of electricity. Faraday wrapped two coils of wire round two sides of an iron ring. He connected the ends of one coil of wire to a galvanometer, a device for measuring current that had been invented by the German physicist Johann **Schweigger** in 1820. The other ends he connected to a battery. When he connected or disconnected the battery he noticed a deflection in the galvanometer. His breakthrough came because he connected the galvanometer to the coil *before* connecting the battery circuit. An electric current was induced in the coil when the magnetic field was changing, not when it was constant. This was electromagnetic induction, and his device was what we now know as a transformer. He repeated the experiment using a bar magnet moving within a coil of wire with the same result. He also made a 'dynamo' by rotating a copper disc between the poles of a magnet, and extracting the current from contacts at the centre and the rim of the disc. The whole of modern industrial society depends on electromagnetic induction, the conversion of mechanical energy into electrical energy by means of a dynamo or generator.

Faraday, together with his friend the classical scholar William **Whewell** (who suggested that the word 'scientist' should be used for those engaged in science), contributed many words and ideas to science. The positive electrode he called the anode, from the Greek $\alpha\upsilon\alpha$, towards, and the negative the cathode, from the Greek $\kappa\alpha\tau\alpha$ – away from, and $o\delta o\sigma$, a way. The word electrolyte was the solution in which electrolysis occurred. He also held that electric charges and magnets had a 'field' around them. He introduced the concept of Specific Inductive Capacity (Dialectric Constant) of various substances. This is their ability to store an electric charge. He was the first to liquefy gases. He showed that the plane of polarised light could be rotated by a magnetic field. This suggested that light was an electromagnetic phenomenon.

His ideas were further developed by William Thompson (Lord Kelvin), James Clerk Maxwell, Oliver Heaviside, G. F. Fitzgerald and Oliver Lodge later in the century, and led Einstein to formulate his theories. He was elected FRS in 1824. He was offered a knighthood but refused as he felt that such preferences were contrary to his socialist principles. He was a member of a rather strict religious sect called the Sandemanians, and later became an elder of that Church. Another branch of the Sandeman family is perhaps better known as the purveyors of the fortified wine known as port. However having refused all honours his name is immortalised in the unit of capacitance, the *farad*. This is the capacity of a capacitor (or condenser) in which a charge of one coulomb raises the potential between its plates of one volt. This is too large for practical purposes and the common unit is the microfarad, 10^{-6} farad, or the picofarad, 10^{-12} farad. The capacitance of a submarine cable about one-third of a nautical mile long is one microfarad.

Joseph **Henry** (1797–1878) was an American physicist who discovered the principle of electromagnetic induction independently and at the same time as Faraday, but as Faraday had published first, he was credited with the discovery. Henry also invented the relay and the principle of the electric telegraph, using the Earth as a return conductor. His method was adapted by the American Samuel **Morse** who is credited with inventing the telegraph. Henry also developed the electromagnet and an oscillating electric motor. In 1846 he became the first secretary of the *Smithsonian* Institution. His work in meteorology led to the establishment of the US Weather Bureau. Under his leadership scientific progress was encouraged and he established a forum for the publication of scientific papers. His name is remembered in the unit of electromagnetic induction. The Henry is defined as the inductance of a closed circuit in which an electromotive force of one volt is produced when an electric current changes uniformly at the rate of one ampere per second.

George Simon **Ohm** (1787–1854) was a German physicist who published a pamphlet in 1827 in Berlin outlining the principles of resistance in an electric circuit. This has been embodied in Ohm's Law, which states that, at a constant temperature, the current I in a circuit is directly proportional to the applied voltage E and inversely proportional to the resistance R in that circuit.

$$I = E/R$$

This is a general expression relating to the flow of a fluid, such as water, in a system. The higher the pressure, the greater the flow; the greater the resistance to that flow, the less will be the flow. Ohm was awarded the Copley medal of the Royal Society in 1841, and his name is remembered in the unit of electrical resistance the *ohm*.

The discovery of the *electron*. Faraday had done numerous experiments with the discharge of electric currents through glass tubes but at the time could not obtain a vacuum high enough to demonstrate the nature of the discharges. In 1854 a German glass blower, Heinrich **Geissler**, produced an effective pump to reduce the air pressure to very low levels. When an electric current was passed through the tube by means of electrodes sealed in the glass, it was noted that a green glow appeared on the wall of the tube, opposite the negative electrode which was called the cathode after Faraday's notation, hence the rays were called *cathode rays* by the German physicist Eugen **Goldstein** in 1876. The English scientist Sir William **Crooks** (who had earlier discovered the element thallium using the spectroscope) improved the Geissler tube and showed that the cathode rays were deflected by a magnet.

In 1897 the English physicist Sir J. J. **Thomson** showed that the rays were deflected by an electric field as well. He determined the ratio of the mass to the charge of these rays proving that they were in fact extremely light particles, with a mass less that 1/1000 that of the hydrogen atom, they were called *electrons* after a suggestion by the Irish physicist George **Stoney** in 1891. Thomson also showed that these particles were also emitted by metals when struck by ultra-violet radiation – the photoelectric effect. He received the Nobel Prize for physics in 1906.

In 1873 James **Clerk Maxwell** wrote the *Treatise on Electricity and Magnetism* predicting the existence of electromagnetic radiation. He showed that the ratio of the electrostatic constant to the magnetic constant was equal to the velocity of light, and that light was therefore an electromagnetic phenomenon, confirming Faraday's belief. His equations relating electric and magnetic fields and time were developed by Oliver **Lodge** (who invented the sparking plug for cars), Oliver **Heaviside**, and George **Fitzgerald**, and led to the prediction of the existence of radio waves which was demonstrated by Heinrich Hertz. The *maxwell* is the CGS unit of magnetic flux.

In 1877 Heinrich Rudolf **Hertz** (1857–1894) demonstrated the existence of such radiation with a spark discharge between two small spheres connected to two large metal plates. Waves with a wavelength of about 2 metres were detected using a circular loop of wire, with a gap which sparked, when placed a multiple of the wavelength from the transmitter. He also demonstrated reflection and polarisation of the waves. His name is commemorated in the unit of frequency; the hertz is one cycle of alternating current per second.

On November 5th, 1895 the German physicist Wilhelm **Röntgen** was studying the effect of luminescence produced by cathode rays. His cathode ray tube was in a black box, and he had darkened the room. When he turned on the tube, he noticed a flash of light from a distant sheet of paper coated with barium platinocyanide. When he turned off the tube the light stopped. Having no idea what these rays were, he called them *X-rays*. An attempt to call them Roentgen rays has not been successful as English people find it hard to pronounce the German correctly.

This was a ground-breaking discovery. It became clear that the radiation was extremely penetrating. It could be detected by its effect on the silver ions in a photographic plate, reducing them to atoms of silver which could then be developed to produce an image (similar to light photography). Bone, containing calcium, appeared dense on an X-ray, as the calcium atoms blocked the radiation, as did lead, and could be used to identify foreign bodies such as bullets. But more important was their ability to ionise a gas, knocking an electron off the atom and giving it an electric charge, which could then be measured by its ability to conduct an electric current. The effect of ionising radiation is to cause heating of the material it hits, but in addition, it can destroy the DNA in living tissues. This effect is used in radiotherapy, as rapidly dividing cells are more sensitive to destruction than normal cells (one problem is that endothelial cells also divide rapidly).

Roentgen was the first to receive the Nobel Prize for physics, which had been instituted in 1901. His name is commemorated in the roentgen, the unit of radiation exposure. It was originally the amount of radiation that would produce one electrostatic unit of electricity in one cubic centimetre of air. In 1918

Russ suggested that the rad (equal to the roentgen) should be the dose of radiation enough to kill a mouse. The rad (radiation absorbed dose) was then introduced in 1953. The rem (roentgen equivalent man) was also suggested. It was replaced in 1980 by the *sievert*, the radiation producing one joule per kilogram. One Sv equals 100 rem. There was a problem in that there is a difference between the estimated dose and the absorbed dose, which is the Gray. Background radiation is of the order of a few microsieverts per hour. The wavelength of X-rays is from 10 to 0.001 nanometres. The shorter the wavelength the more penetrating the radiation. The wavelength depends on the voltage applied to the cathode ray tube. 50-80Kv is used in diagnostic X-rays, 250Kv in radiotherapy. The energy of the electrons can be expressed in electron-volts, and is related to the wavelength of the resulting radiation. Gamma rays have an even shorter wavelength and hence more energy and greater penetration. 'Cosmic' rays even more.

Gamma rays are produced when the atomic nucleus disintegrates. Cosmic rays come from outer space. These radiations can be detected by their ability to ionise a gas in a 'cloud chamber', a device invented by the English physicist C.T.R. **Wilson** in 1893. The ionised gas causes condensation of water particles when the pressure is suddenly reduced, which can be recorded photographically.

When the anode of the cathode tube is struck with electrons, X-rays of a characteristic penetrating power are emitted, depending on the metal used in the anode, a discovery made by the British physicist C. C. **Barkla** in 1911. The German physicist **von Laue** found that X-rays could be diffracted by a crystal and form a pattern on a photographic plate. In England William Laurence and William Henry **Bragg**, father and son, developed an accurate method of calculating the wavelength of an X-ray from its diffraction pattern, and further that the exact orientation of atoms in crystals could be determined. Thus originated the science of X-ray *crystallography*, used years later to establish the structure of DNA.

In 1914 the English physicist H. G-J **Moseley** found that the wavelengths of X-rays emitted by various elements decreased in a regular manner as one went up the periodic table. From this originated the concept of atomic number, that elements could be numbered from 1, hydrogen, to 92, uranium, and that these numbers gave an important clue as to the structure of the atom in the corresponding element. Moseley was to die at the age of 28 in the appalling calamity that was Gallipoli in 1915, during the First World War.

In 1896 the French physicist Antoine-Henri **Becquerel** (1852-1908) took some potassium uranyl sulphate, made fluorescent by exposure to sunlight, and wrapped it in black paper. He found that it would darken a photographic plate, suggesting. that X-rays had been emitted. He then put it aside and waited for the Sun to return, to repeat the experiment. Impatiently, he decided to develop the photographic plates anyway. To his astonishment he found that the plates were deeply darkened by intense radiation. It was quickly found that it was coming from the uranium atoms in the potassium uranyl sulphate. The becquerel is the unit of radioactivity: 37×10^9 becquerels equals one curie, the radiation from one gram of radium. The becquerel is equal to one nuclear disintegration per second.

A young Polish chemist Marie **Sklodowska** (1867–1934), later Curie, became interested in the phenomenon which she called radioactivity. These penetrating rays were called γ-rays (gamma-rays) to distinguish them from α-rays (helium nuclei), and β rays, electrons. She and her husband Pierre developed a technique for measuring radioactivity by its effect in ionising air, which would then conduct an electric current which could be measured.

She found that the element thorium was radioactive, and that there was more radioactivity in the uranium ore pitchblende than could be accounted for by its uranium content. Therefore another element must be present, in minute quantities. The Curies obtained tons of pitchblende and laboriously refined it in a small shack under very primitive conditions and by 1898 had obtained a black powder 400 times more radioactive than uranium. She called it 'Polonium' after her native land. But pitchblende contained an even greater source of radioactivity and they eventually discovered **radium**.

For four years the Curies worked on the purification process and by 1903 had collected enough to be visible and to determine its atomic weight. She presented her PhD dissertation in 1903 and was awarded, along with her husband Pierre and Becquerel, the Nobel Prize for physics. The curie, named in her honour, is the unit of radiation, defined as the amount of radiation in equilibrium with its breakdown product radon, in 1 gram of radium. Or the quantity of radioactive substance undergoing 37×10^9 disintegrations per second.

The Curies also did important work on the phenomenon of **piezo-electricity**, in which deformity of crystals such as rochelle salt, (sodium potassium tartrate) and quartz, causes an electric charge to appear on another face. Likewise, an electric charge causes deformity of a crystal. Thus crystals of lead zirconate titanate are used medically in **ultrasound** instruments, and in sonar (asdic) detectors in underwater surveillance. A short pulse is emitted and the time taken for its return gives a measure of the distance. More elaborate instruments coupled to computers and monitors are used in obstetric scans.

Radioactivity is the emanation from the disintegration of the nucleus of an unstable atom. There are 3 elements:

1. Alpha particles are the nuclei of helium atoms. They have little penetrating power, being stopped by a sheet of paper.

2. Beta particles are electrons, produced by the disintegration of neutrons, which emit an electron and become a proton, beta decay.

3. Gamma radiation, very short wave high frequency electro-magnetic waves with great energy and penetrating power.

A brief interlude for applied science. The theory and practice of alternating electric currents were developed by the Croatian Nikola **Tesla** (1856–1943). He emigrated to the USA in 1884 and demonstrated that electric currents could be generated and transmitted with vastly greater efficiency using alternating voltages, in which the polarity changes rapidly – 50 or 60 times a second. The use of transformers to raise and lower the voltage led to the fact that large amounts of electricity could be transmitted using thinner conductors. His ideas were rejected by Edison but adopted with enthusiasm by George Westinghouse and used with great success at Niagara Falls, and have now been universally adopted.

In 1896, Guglielmo **Marconi**, emigrated to England as he found the Italian authorities were not interested in the possibilities of the new technique of 'wireless telegraphy'. The same year he demonstrated his invention to the Postmaster General, Sir William Preece, by sending a signal from the roof of the Post Office in St Martin's le Grand to a building in Queen Victoria Street, and later that year his ideas were demonstrated at the Royal Institution.

In 1897 he sent signals across the Bristol Channel and the Solent. On 12 December 1901 he sent a signal across the Atlantic from Poldhu in Cornwall to Signal Hill, Newfoundland using a spark transmitter coupled to an aerial several hundred feet long held aloft by kites and balloons (these frequently blew away). This marked the realisation that wireless telegraphy was to be taken seriously and was not just a freak. Apart from enthusiasm his contribution to communication was to add the 'elevated electrode' or aerial (antenna). His transmitter operated at 20,000 volts from a 28,000kVA alternator.

In 1905 he used an arc transmitter at 12,000 volts D.C. at about 82 KHz to achieve two-way Atlantic telegraphy in daylight. In 1926 the British Government contracted the Marconi Company to establish stations to communicate with the Empire and the station at Rugby used thermionic valves at 350kW and achieved world wide coverage, at 19kHz – GBR. The aerial was 38km in circumference supported by 12 masts 250m high. It is still in use for transmission of time signals.

Reception of signals was achieved by rectification – a 'coherer' using iron filings or a *'cat's whisker'*, which was a tiny controllable iron wire which was made to touch an active zone on a crystal of lead sulphide, galena. This was the first 'solid state' electronic device and eventually led to the development of the junction diode and thence, transistor. Marconi developed a system of tuning, syntony, devised by Oliver Lodge, using variable capacitors. He patented his ideas and became a wealthy man. His name is remembered in the name given to a quarter-wavelength vertical end fed aerial - the Marconi.

On Friday, 10 July 1910, the following message was received, transmitted by Snr Marconi's spark transmitter aboard the S.S. *Montrose*, 5,431 tons, Capt. Henry Kendall, Master, en route to Quebec, at Scotland Yard: '3pm GMT Friday 130 miles west Lizard have strong suspicions that Crippen London Cellar murderer and accomplice are amongst saloon passengers moustache taken off growing beard accomplice dressed as boy voice manner and build undoubtedly a girl both travelling as Mr J. and Master Robinson Kendall.'

This was relayed to Inspector Dew at Scotland Yard. Dew travelled to Liverpool and, three days later, set out in a faster ship than the Montrose, the S.S. *Laurentic*. The *Laurentic* overtook the *Montrose* at Father Point, just off Quebec, on 27 July, and Inspector Dew boarded the *Montrose* and arrested Dr Crippen, (Operation Handcuff) for the murder of his wife, a music hall singer who called herself Belle Elmore (born Kunigunde Meckamotzki in Brooklyn, New York).

Hawley Crippen (also American, born in Coldwater, Michigan in 1862) was alleged to have murdered her by administering hyoscine, and buried her torso in the cellar of his house, 39 Hilldrop Crescent, Holloway, London, where it had been found by Dew. Crippen was tried and found guilty. His appeal on 5 November was rejected, and a petition for reprieve was turned down by the Home Secretary, Winston Churchill. He was hanged at Pentonville Goal at 9am on Wednesday morning, 23 November. His 'accomplice', Ethel LeNeve (real name Neave), with whom he was in love, was acquitted.

A sad and sorry tale, at the time causing a great sensation, brought to light the possibilities of wireless telegraphy. 'Trapped by Wireless' ran the headlines, making into a melodrama the story which has over the decades since inspired many writers. Captain Kendall received £500 for his help but many felt he was exceeding his duties as a ship's captain by becoming a police informer.

Spark transmitters were soon to be replaced by thermionic valves (called tubes in the USA).

In 1883, the American inventor Thomas **Edison** noticed that an electric current flowed from the hot filament of one of his lamps to a wire sealed into the lamp, his only contribution to pure science (Edison, together with the English Sir Joseph **Swan**, invented the electric light bulb). He noted it and forgot about it as it did not seem to have any practical purpose.

In 1904 the English electrical engineer John Ambrose **Fleming**, surrounded the hot filament with a cylinder of metal, which he called a plate, and noted that if a positive voltage was applied to this plate, a current would flow as the negative electrons were attracted. If a negative voltage were to be applied, no current would flow as the electrons were repelled. Therefore if an alternating current were applied, rectification would occur as the current would only flow in one direction.

In 1907 the American inventor Lee **De Forest** inserted a metal mesh between the hot filament and the plate. This was the grid, and small variations in the negative voltage on the grid could cause quite large variations in the current flowing to the plate. Thus small signals could be greatly amplified and wireless (now called radio) became feasible, and this marked the development of electronics.

These valves or tubes had to operate in a total vacuum, and used large amounts of energy in heating the hot filament (cathode), the source of electrons, and were comparatively inefficient, and liable to failure, and they have been superseded by transistors.

Now back to pure science...

MAGNETISM

In 1600 William **Gilbert**, physician to Queen Elizabeth I, published a book, *De Magnete*. This was the first scientific description of the phenomenon of magnetism, based on observation and experimentation. Magnetism had been observed by the

Chinese 2,400 years BC, and the Norwegians in the eleventh century AD, using the word 'lodestone' – direction stone. The word magnet is derived from the ancient Greek town of Magnesia, where there were extensive deposits of magnetite, an ore consisting of iron oxides. Gilbert (who coined the word electricity) differentiated between electric forces and magnetic forces and demonstrated that the Earth is a giant magnet.

In 1269 the French scholar Peter **Peregrinus** had named the magnetic poles North and South, and the compass came into use for navigational purposes.

In 1820 the Danish physicist Hans Christian **Oersted** showed that a magnetic needle aligned itself at right angles to a conductor carrying an electric current.

In 1831 Michael Faraday showed that a changing magnetic field would induce an electric current in a coil of wire.

In 1845 Faraday showed that different substances behaved differently in a magnetic field. Iron, cobalt and nickel could be strongly magnetised, and were called ferromagnetic: bismuth and antimony were weakly repelled by a magnetic field and were called diamagnetic: aluminium, platinum and oxygen were weakly attracted and were called paramagnetic. Heusler's alloy, made of copper, aluminium and manganese, is strongly ferromagnetic.

Atoms with odd numbers of hadrons (protons and neutrons) are paramagnetic. When substances containing such atoms, such as water, which contains the hydrogen atom with but a single proton in its nucleus, is put in an intense magnetic field, the protons become realigned. A pulse of radiofrequency energy is applied and the protons start spinning and their axis of rotation is deflected. As they return to ground state – precession – they emit another radiofrequency signal which can be detected. This is the principle underlying *MRI scanning.*

Another property of magnetic materials is the critical, or curie, temperature. When a magnetised metal such as iron is heated, it loses its magnetism at a certain temperature, in the case of iron 769°C, nickel 356°C, cobalt 1075°C.

The nature of magnetic attraction is attributed to magnetic domains, a term suggested in 1907 by the French physicist Pierre

Weiss. These are groups of atoms of iron arranged in such a manner as to become aligned. X-ray crystallography has shown that at normal temperatures, each iron atom is surrounded by 8 neighbours, forming a cube of 9 atoms. When heated to the critical temperature the arrangement changes, the domains break their alignment, and each atom is surrounded by 12 neighbours, accompanied by a tiny noise, the **Barkhausen** effect.

Present theory suggests that magnetism is an intrinsic property of electron spin. In 1896 the Dutch physicist Pieter **Zeeman** showed that the Sodium D lines in a spectroscope were split into 3 when the sodium vapour was placed in an intense magnetic field – the Zeeman effect.

In 1925 the Dutch physicists **Goudsmit** and **Uhlenberg** suggested that this could be explained if it was assumed that the electron in the outer shell of the sodium atom had an intrinsic spin as well as its orbital angular momentum, with quantum numbers $+^1/_2$ $-^1/_2$. Which takes us to the intriguing subject of *quantum mechanics*.

QUANTUM MECHANICS
(T. Davis cartoon courtesy *Private Eye*)

In 1900 the German physicist Max **Planck** (1858–1847) suggested that radiation was not continuous but came in discrete units called quanta (Latin: how much. Cf Spanish: *cuanta es?* – how much is it?), just as matter is not continuous but exists in discrete atoms and molecules, and that the energy of a quantum is proportional to the frequency – $e = hv$, where h is Planck's constant, and v (*nu* – the Greek n) is the frequency.

'Quantum mechanics describes the atom in terms of mathematical interpretations of observed phenomena.' Another statement is that 'quantum mechanics is concerned with specific changes in rotational energy states of atoms and molecules.'

In 1926 the German physicist Erwin **Schrodinger** pictured the atom as a nucleus with a series of stationary waves surrounding it. These waves have crests at certain points, each standing wave representing an orbit. 'The absolute square of the amplitude of the wave at any point is a measure of the probability that an electron will be found at a given time'. This was an expression of **Heisenberg**'s uncertainty principle, that one can determine the position of an electron, or its velocity, but not both at the same time.

The nature of electromagnetic radiation remains an enigma. It has certain properties of 'particles' (difficult to define). At the same time, it has the properties of a wave motion – polarisation, diffraction, interference. Yet a wave has to have a medium, and no medium can be found. For years it was thought to be the luminiferous 'ether', Aristotle's fifth element. But light waves are transverse, undulating at right angles to the direction of motion and could only be transmitted in a solid medium. Assuming the Earth to be travelling through this ether, it should be possible to determine the rate of progress. In 1887, the American scientists A.A. Michelson and E.W. Morley used an interferometer, invented by Michelson, to determine this. But no such velocity could be found, no matter in which direction the light waves were projected. The notion of absolute motion and absolute space seemed no longer tenable. The foundations of physics tottered.

In 1893 the Irish physicist George **Fitzgerald** suggested that this could be explained if matter contracts in its direction of motion and that the amount of the contraction increases with the velocity of motion. $L^1 = L \sqrt{1 - v^2/c^2}$, where L^1 is the length of a body with a velocity of v, when its rest length is L, and c is the velocity of light.

The Dutch physicist H. A. **Lorentz** suggested that a similar transformation could be applied to mass, assuming that the mass of a particle is inversely proportional to its radius, and in 1900 the German physicist W. Kauffman showed that the electrons in cathode rays increased in mass with velocity - $M^1 = M/\sqrt{1-v^2/c^2}$, where M^1 is the mass of a body with a rest mass of M moving with a velocity v, and c is the velocity of light.

In England, between 1906 and 1908 the New Zealand-born physicist Ernest **Rutherford** (1871–1937) was bombarding a thin foil of gold with α-particles, helium nuclei, derived from a piece of radium, recording their presence on a photographic plate. Most of them passed through, but there was an unexpected scattering around the central spot, and some of them appeared to bounce back. The explanation was that they had collided with a dense central structure, the nucleus of the atom, consisting of protons (the diameter of the nucleus is only 1/100,000 that of the whole atom, but most of the mass of the atom is there). This was the first demonstration of the internal structure of the atom.

Rutherford showed that alpha rays were weakly deflected to the left in a strong magnetic field, showing that they were positively charged and had a relatively high mass, and beta rays were strongly deflected to the right, showing that they were of small mass and negatively charged. Alpha rays are absorbed by a thin sheet of metal or a few centimetres of air, and are helium nuclei. Beta rays are more penetrating and are identical with cathode rays and are electrons. Gamma rays are similar to X-rays, electromagnetic radiation with very short wavelengths, high frequency, very penetrating, and are not influenced by electric or magnetic fields.

In 1913 the Danish physicist Niels **Bohr** (1885–1962) pictured the hydrogen atom as consisting of a central nucleus surrounded by an electron that could occupy a number of fixed orbits, each orbit representing an energy level, and that when an electron changes its orbit, losing energy, light of a specific wavelength is emitted, as detected in the spectroscope. A *photon* in fact, a term that was introduced by the American physicist Arthur Holly **Compton** in 1928. Compton also noted that X-rays, when scattered by colliding with other particles, lose energy and their wavelength increases – the Compton effect.

Present theory infers that the nucleus of the atom is surrounded by 'shells' of electrons, in definite patterns, labelled K,L,M,N,O,P. The K shell contains 2 electrons and is stable, the inert gas helium (atomic number 2) falls into this group. A 'saturated' shell has 8 electrons, and the inert gases neon, argon, krypton, xenon, fall into this group being extremely unreactive. The outer electrons are the valence electrons, the number corresponding to the 'valency' of the atom, which is the number of other atoms it will react with. Thus sodium (atomic number 11, 2+8+1 electrons in its shells) has one spare electron, and has a valency of plus 1, and will react with a chlorine (atomic number 17, 2+8+7 electrons in its shells) and hence a valency of minus one. The notion is that an electron is shared between the sodium and the chlorine atom, and in the dry state forms a crystal with a cubic structure, common salt. When dissolved in water, the electrons are lost and the sodium atom develops a positive charge and migrates towards the negative electrode the cathode, in electrolysis, and is a *cation*. The negative chlorine atom migrates towards the positive anode and is an *anion*.

Hydrogen has one electron and has a valency of +1. Oxygen (atomic number 8, 2+6 electrons) has 6 outer electrons and has a valency of -2. Thus water is H_2O. But water dissociates into hydrogen, a single proton, with a valency of +1, and hydroxyl OH, with a valency of -1. The dissociation is very small, only 10^{-14} grams per litre. When there is an excess of hydrogen ions, the solution becomes acid, when there is an excess of hydroxyl ions the solution becomes alkaline. The *Ph* is the logarithm of the hydrogen ion concentration with the sign reversed. Thus neutral Ph is 7.0. Acids have a lower pH, alkalis a higher one.

Carbon (atomic number 6, 2+4 electrons) has an excess or a deficiency of 4 and has a valency of 4. Silicon (atomic number 14) and germanium (atomic number 32) also have a valency of 4.

These considerations are important in understanding the operation of junction transistors. But first, one must understand the nature of electrical conductors and insulators, why some materials conduct electricity and others do not (these terms were suggested by the French inventor **Desaguliers** in 1740).

Transmission of electricity occurs in a similar manner to the transmission of heat, that is to say, by conduction , convection and radiation.

Conduction occurs when atoms, with spare electrons in their outer shells (commonly metals), and are closely bound as in solids. These are called valency or conduction bands. *Resistance* is the property of a substance to oppose the conduction of a current. Silver, copper and aluminium have low resistance and are good conductors. Resistance is dependent upon temperature, and as a general rule the higher the temperature the greater the resistance. Conversely, the lower the temperature, the lower the resistance, and the better the conductor, until at very low temperatures the substance becomes a ***superconductor***.

In 1908 the Dutch physicist H.K. **Onnes** succeeded in liquifying the gas helium, at a temperature of 4.2K, a temperature at which all other substances are solid. In 1911 he found that the resistance of mercury fell to zero at 4.12K and that an electric current started in the mercury would continue indefinitely. This was the phenomenon of *superconductivity*. Lead became superconducting at 7.22K and a current induced in a ring of lead, kept at that temperature by liquid helium, continued to circulate for $2^1/_2$ years. Recently materials have been found that become superconducting at much higher temperatures, but as yet to find useful applications, as they are difficult to make into wires. A superconducting magnet is used in medicine in MRI scanners.

Convection requires an additional medium to convey the electrons. Typically these are ions in a solution of an electrolyte.

Radiation occurs typically when a high frequency (>15kHz) alternating electric current is connected to a conductor, the aerial or antenna. Electrons become photons, and in the receiving aerial, the photons become electrons again and can be amplified. This is the basis of radio communication.

There is an additional means of transmission of an electric current which could be called *direct transfer*. This occurs in a cathode ray tube when a stream of electrons passes through a vacuum under the influence of an electric field.

Insulators have no spare electrons.

In 1947 the American physicists J. **Bardeen**, W.H. **Brattain**, and W.B. **Shockley**, at the Bell Telephone laboratories, were working with semi-conductors such as silicon and germanium, whose conductivities seemed to be improved when they contained trace elements. Germanium atom (atomic number 32) has 4 unpaired electrons in its outer shell, which pair up with the 4 of a neighbouring atom, with no spare electrons so it does not conduct.

Arsenic (atomic number 33) has 5 electrons in its outer shell and if a trace (1 part per million) is added to the germanium, it takes the place of a germanium atom in the crystal lattice and there is then a spare electron, causing better conductivity. This arrangement is called n-type as it has spare electrons, acting as if it were negatively charged.

Boron (atomic number 5 – 2+3) has 3 electrons in its outer shell, and when a trace is added to germanium it takes its place in the lattice but there is then a deficiency of one electron, in effect a 'hole', and if an electric current is passed, the electrons fill the hole and the material conducts. This arrangement is called p-type as it accepts electrons, acting as if it were positively charged.

Later silicon, also valency 4, was found to be better than germanium and is used as the substrate now. Also phosphorus, and antimony can be used as n-type (5 valency electrons) and gallium and indium as p-type (3 valency electrons).

P-n or n-p junctions will only conduct electric currents one way and act as rectifiers.

When p-n-p (or n-p-n) junctions are made they become a *transistor*. The three elements are the emitter, the base and the

Sculpture 'Ex tenebris Lux' by Ernest Gillick at the Robert McDougall Art Gallery in Christchurch New Zealand.

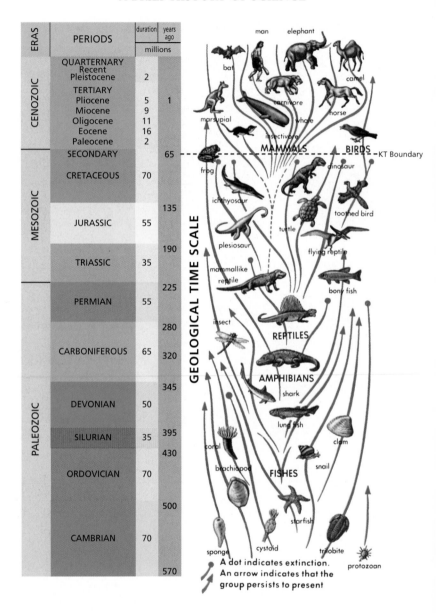

Geological Timetable - based upon *Geology* by Frank H.T. Rhodes. Golden Press Western Publishing Company Inc. Racine, Wisconsin.

Carl Linnaeus, naturalist, dressed in traditional Saami (Lapp) costume. Engraved by Henry Kingsbury and published in 1805. He was not considered clever enough to become a priest, so he became a doctor. The Bridgeman Art Library.

Portrait of Sir Benjamin Thompson, Count Rumford, by Thomas Gainsborough. American adventurer, philosopher, philanthropist, philanderer. Joint founder of the Royal Institution. Courtesy of the Fogg Art Museum, Harvard University Art Museums, Bequest of Edmund C. Converse. Photo credit: Photographic Services. Image Copyright: © 2003 President and Fellows of Harvard College.

Portrait of Sir Joseph Banks by Sir Joshua Reynolds. Looking relaxed and confident, as well he might, considering the time he had spent in the bed of a Tahitian princess. Later President of the Royal Society. The genus of Australian shrubs *Banksia* is named after him. The Bridgeman Art Library.

Portrait of Thomas Henry Huxley by Alphonse Legros. He was
the grandfather of the novelist Aldous *Brave New World* Huxley.
The Bridgeman Art Library.

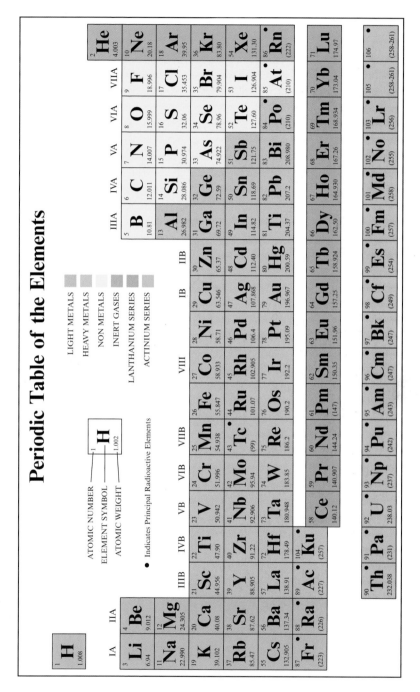

Periodic Table of the Elements

Frequency in hertz (cycles per second) (v)

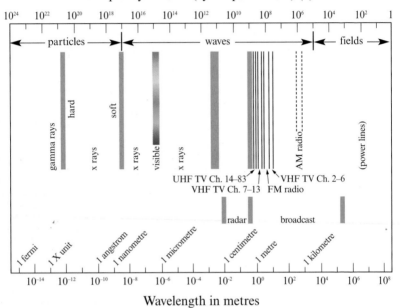

$v\lambda = c = 300,000$ km/sec $= 3 \times 10^8$ m/sec

The Electromagnetic Spectrum.

collector, and act as a current amplifier when connected in a suitable circuit, similar to a triode valve. Nowadays integrated circuits contain many hundreds if not thousands of such transistors in a small unit. By 2002 55 million junctions measuring 150 nanometres each could be packed into a 'chip' no bigger than a postage stamp.

In 1906 Albert **Einstein** published *On the Electrodynamics of Moving Bodies*. Just as the error in the orbit of the planet Mars found by Brahe and Kepler to be 8 minutes of arc, led to the ideas of Copernicus prevailing and the abandonment of the Ptolemaian geocentric nature of the universe, so the error of 43 seconds per century of the perihelion of the planet Mercury found by Leverrier, led to the adoption of the ***Relativity*** Theory of the nature of physical forces, suggested by Einstein.

This presupposed that time and space were not distinct entities, but existed in a space/time continuum and that apparent forces such as gravity could be explained by accelerations in this continuum by the existence of mass.

He calculated that $E = mc^2$, which proved devastatingly correct when the world's first atomic bomb was exploded at 5.30 am on 16 July 1945 at Alamogordo, New Mexico, USA, a detonation equivalent to 20,000 tons of TNT, the commencement of the Atomic Age.

In 1930 two German physicists **Bothe** and **Becker** bombarded beryllium atoms with α-particles, producing radiation of great penetrating power. The English physicist James **Chadwick** used these particles to bombard boron atoms. He found that the increase in mass corresponded with that of the proton, but these particles could not be detected in a cloud chamber so they had no charge. This was the ***neutron***, and atomic nuclei consisted of protons and neutrons, a concept that explained the nature of ***isotopes***.(Greek ισο – same, τοπι – place). The number of protons in the nucleus was the atomic number, balanced by the number of electrons in the shell, which gave the atom its chemical properties and affinities. Its atomic weight was determined by the total number of protons and neutrons.

Isotopes contained additional neutrons. Thus hydrogen has one proton and one electron. Its isotope **deuterium** (written H^2 or D) has one proton and one neutron in the nucleus, and one electron. It has the same chemical properties as hydrogen but twice the atomic weight. 'Heavy' water is deuterium oxide, D_2O. Deuterium was discovered in 1932 by the chemist Harold **Urey**. Adding a further neutron produces hydrogen 3, or **tritium**, which is highly radioactive and very unstable with a half life at eighteen years. It emits an electron (beta-decay) and becomes helium 3.

Also in 1930 the English physicist Paul **Dirac** predicted the existence of an anti-particle, the anti-electron. This was detected in 1932 by the American Carl **Anderson** using very high energy cosmic rays in a cloud chamber and called a **positron**. These have a very short 'life', and, as soon as one meets an electron, which is quite soon as the universe is full of electrons, they annihilate each other with a flash of gamma rays. This transformation works in reverse, as a gamma-ray can suddenly become an electron and a positron, 'pair production'.

By 1937 the Italian physicist Enrico **Fermi** had identified 37 different isotopes by neutron bombardment, the neutrons being slowed down by water or paraffin, the better to enable the nucleus of the atom to capture one. When a nucleus captures a neutron its atomic number is unchanged because there is no increased charge, but its atomic weight increases and it becomes unstable. It may then break up and emit radiation. Fermi bombarded uranium (atomic number 92) with neutrons and found that a new element atomic number 93 was found. But in the breakdown products radioactive Barium was found. Otto **Hahn** and Lise **Meitner** worked on the problem.

In 1938 Germany occupied Austria and Lise Meitner, who was Jewish, was forced to flee to Sweden. In a letter to *Nature* in January 1939 she suggested that the unstable element 93 had broken into two, forming barium (58) and what was later identified as technetium (43). This she called nuclear fission, and was accompanied by the emission of large amounts of energy and 2 or 3 neutrons. These spare neutrons can then enter further uranium nuclei causing these to break up – a chain reaction.

It was found that the isotope uranium 235 was the one implicated in the fission reaction, and, since it is only present in 0.3% of uranium ore, most of which is U-238, had to be separated out. This was done by gaseous diffusion, using uranium hexafluoride and eventually produced enough enriched uranium to make a chain reaction.

Under the direction of Enrico Fermi, in 1942 an *atomic pile* was constructed in Chicago, under a football stadium. This consisted of layer upon layer of uranium and graphite (a moderator, to slow the neutrons), with cadmium control rods interspersed. It was 32 feet long, 30 feet wide, 21 feet high, weighed 1400 tons and contained 6 tons of uranium, and 50 tons of uranium oxide. (If U235 had been used, it would only have needed to weigh 9 ounces). On 2 December 1942 the cadmium control rods were slowly pulled out and at 3.45pm the multiplication factor had reached 1, and a controlled fission reaction was under way.

When U-238 absorbs a thermal neutron, it becomes U-239, breaking down to neptunium 239 and almost immediately to plutonium 239, which having an odd number of neutrons (145) was likely to be unstable and therefore fissionable. It was found easier to separate plutonium and reactors were establish to make it, at Oak Ridge Tennessee, and at Hanford in the State of Washington.

By 1945 enough U-235 and plutonium was available to make bombs, the first of which was detonated in July 1945, by bringing together two pieces of fissionable material to make a critical mass.

As the perceptive Admiral Yamamoto remarked when the returning Japanese pilots were celebrating the destruction of the American Pacific Fleet at Pearl Harbor on 7 December 1941 'We have tweaked the tail of the Dragon and set him a terrible purpose.' Nemesis shall surely befall those who show hubris.

On 8 August 1945 an atomic bomb was dropped on the Japanese city of Hiroshima, killing about 130,000 people and rendering another 180,000 people homeless. This, together with a bomb on Nagasaki on 9 August, brought to an end to the Second World War, with the possible saving of over a million lives as the Japanese would have fought ferociously to defend their territory.

Plutonium is not very radioactive, with a half-life of 24,000 years but is extremely toxic to living organisms.

The heat from a nuclear reactor using enriched uranium is used to boil water to run a steam turbine to generate electricity.

There are many other 'fundamental particles', such as neutrinos, anti-neutrinos, muons, pions, mesons, quarks, anti-quarks (all 6), wimps, superstrings, etc. Too many for a busy person to get to grips with. These are best left to Professors of Particle Physics.

CHAPTER SIX

BIOLOGY

The Glory of Life is its Diversity.

It is life's infinite variety that makes it difficult to classify, evaluate, and to measure in a scientific manner.

Life is not a means to an end, but an end in itself.

Populations are the reservoirs of genetic diversity and genes are the currency of evolutionary change.'

Life is a dynamic equilibrium in a polyphasic system.
(F.G.Hopkins)

Life has, however, several properties, defined by Claude
Bernard (1813-1878, French Physiologist)
1. *Assimilation and respiration*
2 *Growth and development*
3. *Secretion and excretion*
4. *Reproduction.*
5. *Movement (animals)*

The word Biology was first used about 1800, popularised by the French *savant* **Lamarck**

BASICS

<u>**Water**</u> is essential for life. Without liquid water metabolic processes cannot function. Certain organisms, microbes and plants, can form spores and cysts which are extremely resistant to heat and cold, radiation and drying out. These spores contain genetic material which can survive for years in an inactive state.

They may be present in outer space and provide a possible means of dissemination of life throughout the Universe.

Although water has a simple chemical formula, H_2O, two atoms of hydrogen attached to one of oxygen, it has several remarkable physico-chemical properties:

1. It has a very high boiling point considering its low molecular weight (18). This is due to hydrogen bonding.

2. It has a high dielectric constant – 76 (air = 1). (The property of an insulator to accept an electric charge – sometimes called **Specific Inductive Capacity**).

3. It dissociates into hydrogen ions (protons with a positive charge – H^+) and hydroxyl ions with a negative charge – OH^-. It is this that causes acidity, measured by **Ph**. This notation was introduced by **Sorenson** in 1909. The Ph index of a solution is the logarithm of the hydrogen ion concentration in gram-ions per litre, with the sign reversed. Thus water dissociates to the extent of 10^{-14} gm-ions per litre at 25° Celsius, which means neutral water would have a Ph of 7.0, acid water would have a smaller Ph and alkaline water a greater one.

4. The maximum density of water is at 4° Celsius.

5. The angle between the two hydrogen atoms is 105°, leading to asymmetry.

6. The water molecule is **polar**, that is to say, it develops a positive charge at one end and a negative charge at the other end, causing the molecules to aggregate, which may well be the cause of its relatively high melting and boiling points, as well as its affinity for the amino acids in proteins, which are also polar.

7. The resonant frequency of the water molecule is 2.45GHz, giving it a wavelength of 12.2µ. This is the frequency that microwave cooking ovens work.

8. Under certain circumstances, water crystallizes in hexagonal plates, each one different from another one – snowflakes.

9. When water freezes it expands, reducing its density. Ice floats on water.

The physico-chemical reaction known as **photosynthesis** is the basis of life, the foot of the ladder leading to higher, more complex organisms such as Man. In it, radiant energy from the Sun is transformed into chemical energy, carbohydrate, which is then used to promote the metabolism of the organism. This process is catalysed by enzymes present in the green magnesium-containing pigment *chlorophyll*. The chemical transformation is:

$$6H_2O + 6CO_2 = C_6H_{12}O_6 + 6O_2$$

A photon of light hits an electron of a hydrogen atom in water raising its energy level so that it reacts with a molecule of carbon dioxide, releasing a molecule of oxygen and forming a molecule of carbohydrate. This is the overall reaction, but it is a complex one involving the conversion of ADP (Adenosine diphosphate) to ATP (Adenosine triphosphate) which contains an energy-rich phosphate bond which the organism can use (Calvin Cycle).

Chlorophyll is contained in *chloroplasts*, tiny organelles 4–6μ in diameter, present in all green plants, perhaps as many as 40–50 to a cell and 500,000 to a square millimetre of leaf area. It is thought that chloroplasts may have been descended from cyanobacteria, the most primitive organism.

Certain bacteria use *chemosynthesis*, reactions using sulphur or iron for instance, extracting energy from the reduction of ferric iron to ferrous iron without the necessity for light, but these are insignificant compared with photosynthesis.

$C_6H_{12}O_6$ is the basic formula of *glucose* (or its dextro-rotatory isomer dextrose) sometimes called *hexose* as it contains 6 carbon atoms. These molecules link up to form long chain insoluble molecules of glycogen in animals, starch in plants, used as storage molecules in muscle, liver and potatoes for instance. They can be broken down into soluble glucose (*hydrolysis*) by enzymes and strong acids. In the stomach N/2 hydrochloric acid achieves this.

Plankton are microscopic floating or weakly swimming organisms in the ocean. The grass of the ocean is the *phytoplankton*, algae (seaweeds and sea grass) diatoms, coccolithophore, silico flagellates and dinoflagellates.

The *zooplankton* are the grazers of the ocean, including copepods, foraminifera, pteropods and radiolarians. The herbiverous zooplankton are consumed by the carniverous zooplankton, and they in turn by the higher organisms and fishes. Primitive organisms such as diatoms and sponges have a 'shell' of silica, derived from metasilicic acid (H_2SiO_3) in seawater.

More advanced organisms have a shell made of Calcium Carbonate, derived from dissolved CO_2 in the water. Deposits of billions of shells and ooliths (tiny grains consisting of calcium carbonate deposits on a grain of silica) make up the chalk and limestone strata, during the *Cretaceous* era, 135–65 million years ago.

The *cell* is the fundamental structural unit of all organisms. Cells were first identified by Robert Hooke in 1668 in cork. The cellular theory was further developed by Theodor **Schwann** in 1838 and extended by Rudolf **Virchow** in 1849. 'All cells come from cells'. Cancer cells come from abnormal cells.

Unicellular (or non-cellular) organisms are the bacteria (the streptococcus is 1μ in diameter) and protozoa, down to mycoplasmas, about 100 nanometers (0.1μ) in diameter (viruses are not considered cells as they lack the necessary apparatus to sustain an independent existence. They are obligatory parasites, depending on the machinery of a host cell to replicate).

Multicellular organisms are the rest.

The animal cell consists of a double membrane, 7.5–10 nanometers thick, made of phospholipid. This is selectively semi-permeable, that is to say, water molecules can pass freely through it, but ions and larger molecules cannot, and this process is essential to the structure and function of the cell. Rigidity of the cell is due to *osmotic pressure* caused by the concentration of electrolytes within the cell being higher than that in the surrounding fluid, sap in the case of plants, blood or serum in the case of animals, forcing water into the cell and raising its internal pressure causing rigidity. Outside the membrane lies the *cell wall*, in plants made of the rigid polysaccharide *cellulose*.

Within the cell wall is the *cytoplasm*, and within the cytoplasm is the *nucleus* (at least in the *eukaryotes*. In the *prokary-*

otes – such as bacteria and blue-green algae, the cellular DNA is in direct contact with the cytoplasm). The cytoplasm is made up of 60–65% water in a viscous gel, with a protein matrix supporting the cell.

Within the cytoplasm are various *organelles*, contained within a membrane.

The principal organelle is the nucleus, which contains the *chromosomes* and *genes* of the genetic code made of De-oxy-ribo-nucleic acid (DNA). Chromosomes are organised into long convoluted double helices which split during cell division (*mitosis*) so that each daughter cell contains an exact copy of the mother cell DNA. Prior to division, the cell swells up to double its size. A spindle forms and the chromosomes migrate to the periphery of the spindle, where the purine/pyrimidine hydrogen bonds (adenine/thymine and cytosine/guanine) rupture and the cell divides. The spindle constricts about its equator and the cell splits into two.

In the reproductive organs, ovaries in the female and testes in the male, a reduction division called *meiosis* occurs, in which each daughter cell only contains half the chromosomes of the mother cell (23 in the case of *Homo sapiens* – a sperm producing a female would have 22X and a sperm producing a male offspring would have 22Y configuration. All ova have a 22X, X and Y being the chromosomes determining sex. Or possibly gender). Following fertilization, the full complement of 46 is restored, 44XX in the case of females, 44XY in the case of males. The non-sex chromosomes are called autosomes.

Within the nucleus lies the *nucleolus*, where nucleoprotein particles (messenger RNA) are made. These migrate out into the cytoplasm and become *ribosomes*.

Other organelles are *mitochondria*, the powerhouses of the cell, where glucose and oxygen is used to make ATP which is the basis of energy of the cell. Energy rich phosphate bonds of ATP are used in most biological processes, such as muscle contraction, in which ATP becomes ADP. It is thought that mitochondria may have been descended from purple non-sulphur bacteria.

After 20 years research, in 1994, the British biochemist Dr John **Walker**, together with Prof Paul **Boyer** of the University of California, determined the way ATP (adenosine triphosphate) was made from ADP, adenosine diphosphate. The enzyme *ATP synthase* was extracted from cow's hearts, crystallised, and its structure determined by X-ray crystallography. There are 3000 amino acids in the structure. The enzyme is sausage shaped, one end, the motor, is embedded in the membrane of the mitochondrium, the other, where the ATP is made, dangles into the cell. The membrane end of the enzyme is a molecular wheel, driven by protons, rotating around 100 revolutions a second. Attached to the wheel is a bent axle supported at its other end by a 'hat', which does not rotate, a ring of six protein subunits that are anchored to the mitochondrial membrane and form part of the enzyme that fashions ATP. An ADP molecule within the 'hat' picks up a phosphate molecule and, as the bent axle rotates within the 'hat', it deforms it, squeezing out 3 molecules of ATP with each revolution. A remarkable process, that has been confirmed by the Japanese Professor Masasuke **Yoshido** who attached a muscle fibre protein to the bent axle and observed the rotation under the microscope. It is difficult to explain this in terms of pure Darwinian evolutionary theory.

Plants in addition have *chloroplasts* which contain chlorophyll and convert carbon dioxide and water into sugar under the influence of light. Others described are centrioles and Golgi apparatus.

Inside the cell there is a high concentration of potassium ions. Outside, in the interstitial fluid (lymph) there is a high concentration of sodium ions. The sodium pump, pushing out sodium ions, maintains this differential, which results in a potential difference of 0.1 volt between the inside and the outside of the cell. When the cell is stimulated, the cell 'fires', the potential difference collapses. It takes 2 milliseconds for the cell to recover, during which time it will not respond. This is the refractory period. In the case of a nerve cell, an impulse travels down the axon of the nerve cell and stimulates other nerve cells. A similar process involves muscle cells. It is interesting to note that an 'all or none' mechanism operates with regard to nerve conduction or muscle contraction, similar to the digital or binary mechanism used in computers.

HISTORY

Robert Hooke (1635–1703) curator of experiments of the Royal Society, described the cells of cork, the bark of a tree, in 1665. In 1668 the Dutch haberdasher and chamberlain to the sheriffs of Delft, Antoni van **Leeuwenhoek** (1632–1723) described capillaries, bacteria and spermatozoa using a 300x microscope that he had made, using two lenses. He later described red blood corpuscles. He refused to allow his method to be known so it was not until many years later that his discoveries were confirmed. He also described the life cycle of insects.

The discovery of the circulation of the blood was attributed to William **Harvey** (1578–1657), physician to King James I and Charles I, in his book *De Motu Cordis* (1628), evidence for this being the valves in veins, which only permit one way flow of blood. It must have been clear to butchers and others that blood circulated but this view was contrary to the establishment notion that blood flowed in and out like tides, a doctrine propounded by the anatomist and physician **Galen** (AD129–199).

The *savant* from Navarre (now part of Spain) Miguel Serveto **Servetus** (1511–1553) had described the lesser (pulmonary) circulation in 1546. He had studied law, medicine and theology, but was not convinced of the doctrine of the Trinity. He was accused of heresy. He was tried, convicted, and, on 27 October 1553, was burnt at the stake by Calvin in Geneva. However, to give Calvin his due, he would have preferred to have had him beheaded. Europe was a dangerous place in the Middle Ages (not only in Europe – in 1692 20 'witches' were executed at Salem, Massachusetts). It was a time when Politics was Theology (theocracy) as it still is in certain countries. Today, Politics is largely Economics in 'developed' countries.

Whilst one of the tasks of **Adam** was to name the animals (Genesis 2: v20), it fell to Linnaeus to name the plants (7,700 plants) as well as the animals (4,400 animals). Carl **Linnaeus** (1707–1778) was the eldest son of a Lutheran pastor Nils (who changed his name from Ingemarsson to Linnaeus) and who lived at Rashult (Småland), Southern Sweden. At the age of four he first developed an interest in plants. He had an amazing visual memory (just as Mozart had an amazing auditory memory) but was not considered clever enough to enter the priesthood, to the disappointment of his parents; but his tutor, Dr Rothman, thought he might have 'distinguished and profitable career in medicine.' But his mother thought that he would never rise higher than an Army surgeon.

Even as a student at Uppsala University he earned a precarious living by giving lectures and demonstrations, which were well attended, addressing an audience of 300–400 instead of the usual 70–80. There was a chronic dearth of lecturers.

At the age of 25 he embarked on a journey to Lapland, in the far north of Sweden and collected numerous plants along the way, further developing his ideas. In 1735, then 28, he went to Germany and Holland, and met his greatest benefactor and patron, George **Clifford**, an enormously rich 50-year old Anglo-Dutch financier and director of the Dutch East India Company, who had a garden and private zoo at Hartekamp, his country estate 5 miles from Haarlem, on the way to Leiden, the upkeep of which was said to cost 12,000 gulden a year

There he met the greatest flower painter of the age, the German botanist G.D. **Ehret**, who later settled in England. Linnaeus managed to get the banana tree in Clifford's garden to flower and in 1737 got it to fruit splendidly, the first time a banana had been grown in Europe.

In 1736 he spent a month in London and met the famous physician and naturalist Sir Hans **Sloane**, who had bought the manor of Chelsea in 1712, which he gave to the Society of Apothecaries in 1721, in which lies the Chelsea Physic Garden. Communication was difficult as Linnaeus spoke no English.

In 1735 he published the ***Systema Naturae***, a system of classification of plants and animals, an introduction of order into biology. He described 10,000 species. It was written in Latin, and thereby had a wide readership. Had it been written in

Swedish, it may well have passed unnoticed. Classification is known as **taxonomy** (Greek: ταξισ – arrangement, νομοσ – law). Each plant or animal was given two Latin names (binomial), **Genus**, with a capital letter, and in the case of plants a group of **species** possessing similar organs of fructification (flowers and fruits), and species, with lower case. Thus the cat Genus was *Felix*; a lion was *Felix leo*, a tiger *Felix tigris*. Man was named, somewhat provocatively, *Homo sapiens*. Species did not inter-breed. Or if they did, their offspring were sterile. Thus a cross between a horse and a donkey produced a mule, which was sterile.

In addition different species cannot indulge in 'meaningful' communication. Linnaeus' classification was based on mor-phology, the resemblance of plants (particularly their reproduc-tive organs), and animals to each other, together with their structure and function. No doubt in future classification will be based on DNA analysis.

On 17 June 1739 Linnaeus married Sara Lisa Moraeus, daughter of Dr Johan Moraeus, physician in Falun, to whom he had been betrothed in 1735. Her parents had hoped for a better match than to marry another doctor, but eventually relented.

Having been released from three years of 'wretched drudgery' of medical practice, in 1741 he was appointed Professor of Medicine and Botany at Uppsala University, a post he had long coveted, enabling him to pursue his interest in botany.

In 1753 he was created a Knight of the Polar Star, and in 1761 was ennobled, taking the style of von Linné.

After his death in 1778, his extensive collection, which included 19,000 pressed plants, 3,200 insects, 2,500 mineral specimens, and 3000 books, was bought for 1,000 guineas by James Edward **Smith**, a friend of Sir Joseph Banks, who recog-nised their importance. Smith was knighted in 1814. The Linnaean Society was established in London in 1788, with the collection established in Burlington House, with Smith as its first curator. In 1939 it was moved to a place of safety at Woburn Abbey, as war was imminent.

The Swedes were naturally furious that the collection had left Sweden, but eventually realised that its accessibility in a cosmopolitan centre like London increased Linnaeus' renown.

Today, we have 5 Kingdoms:
1. Prokaryota (Monera) – the microscopic primitive non-cellular organisms, with no nucleus – such as bacteria and blue-green algae (cyanobacteria). Nuclear material is confined to a single loop of DNA, which has about 3000 genes.
2. Protoctista (protista) – protozoa such as amoebae, and the malarial parasite plasmodium vivax. They have nuclei, mainly live in water, can reproduce sexually or asexually. Some can photosynthesise. The slime moulds are classified as protoctista – they are myxomycetes – small amoeboid cells that can unite to form fungi.
3. Fungi – including yeasts, mushrooms and moulds. Assimilate by absorption. Reproduce by spores. Involved in decomposition of dead plant and animal matter.
4. Plants – static, contain chlorophyll, cell wall made of cellulose, can reproduce sexually or asexually.
5. Animals – mobile, feed on plants or other animals, reproduce mainly sexually but some asexually. Have a cell membrane but no cell wall.
A sixth kingdom, the archaebacteria, is described. They are single celled organisms that can convert carbon dioxide and hydrogen to produce methane. They are very hardy and thrive in anaerobic conditions, without oxygen, and may have converted the Earth's primitive atmosphere from CO_2 rich to oxygen rich).

Viruses are minute organisms (0.18-600nm in diameter) that were first identified in 1892 – the Tobacco Mosiac Virus. They are obligatory parasites, are completely dependent on, and reproduce, in living cells. Their structure was not clear until the invention of the electron microscope in 1932. They consist of a single nucleic acid surrounded by a protein layer, forming a nucleocapsid. They attach themselves to a cell, inject their DNA or RNA into it, cause the cell to start making the virus DNA or RNA, the cell then bursts and more viruses are liberated. The *bacteriophages* are viruses that infect bacteria, first discovered in 1912. Viruses are the causative organisms of many diseases such as colds, measles, chickenpox, smallpox, mumps, rubella and AIDS.

Further classifications are as follows, e.g. Man:
  Kingdom – Animal
  Phylum – Chordata: have a notochord – a central nerve cord.
  Subphylum – Vertebrata: animals with backbones, protecting the notochord (only 5% of animals).
  Class – Mammalia: animals with hair. Suckle their young.
  Order – Primates: having fingers with sensitive pads and nails – including monkeys, apes and Lemurs.
  Family – Homidinae: gorilla, chimpanzee, Man. Upright, flat face, large brain.
  Genus – Homo: bi-pedal – large brain.
  Species – *Homo sapiens*: Modern Man, double curved spine, well developed chin.

In 1796 Dr Edward **Jenner**, a Gloucestershire physician and naturalist, inoculated an eight-year old boy, James Phipps, with material obtained from a cowpox vesicle from the hand of a milkmaid, Sarah Nelmes. Six weeks later he inoculated him with material from a virulent smallpox (variola) lesion. Nothing happened. He believed that an infection with cowpox (vaccinia) would lead to immunity to smallpox, based on the ideas and experience of Lady Mary Montague Wortley, wife of the British Ambassador to Turkey, who had seen 'variolation' carried out there and had had her children done. She used liquid from a recovering smallpox patient but it was not always successful.

There was much opposition to Dr Jenner's method at the time, but now the scourge of smallpox has been totally wiped out using epidemiological methods, with no idea as to the nature of the causative organism. Jenner first used the term 'virus', which has subsequently proved correct. He was elected Fellow of the Royal Society, not because of his promotion of vaccination, but on account of his description of the nesting habits of the cuckoo.

Following a fourteen-year campaign, in 1980 the World Health Organisation declared that smallpox had been eradicated worldwide.

The French chemist Louis **Pasteur** (1822–1895) discovered the phenomenon of isomerism, that tartaric acid exists in two forms, one of which rotated the plane of polarised light to the right (dextrorotatory), the other to the left (laevorotatory). But his principal claim to fame lay with his researches on fermentation. He was able to show that milk only went sour when it was in contact with air, due to bacterial contamination. Souring could be prevented by destroying most of the bacteria by heating, a process known as ***pasteurisation***. Milk has to be heated to 63°C for 30 minutes and then rapidly cooled to achieve this, and beer and wine to 60°C for 20 minutes. Unfortunately, pasteurisation does not destroy the tubercle bacillus. His researches into disease prevention led to a vaccine for anthrax in cattle, and more importantly, a vaccine for rabies. He saved the French silk industry, which was being ravaged by disease, by identifying the cause, infected eggs, and only breeding from uninfected ones. His ideas on the germ theory of disease led to Lord **Lister** in England using carbolic acid (phenol) to sterilise wounds, thereby reducing operative mortality. To Pasteur is attributed the saying 'chance favours the mind prepared'.

Charles **Darwin** (1809–1882) abandoned careers in medicine and the Church and embarked on the three-masted barque HMS *Beagle* at the age of 22, on a voyage that was to last five years. He came from a wealthy family and was taken on to provide companionship for the Captain, Robert Fitzroy. They sailed along the east and west coast of South America, Darwin collecting various plants animals and rocks to be sent back to England. On reaching the Galapagos Islands off Ecuador, Darwin was impressed by the 14 species of finch, all with different beaks, adapted to eat seeds, cacti and insects. Studying the theory of **Malthus**, that a population always produced more offspring than its environment could support, outgrew its food supply, so that it was cut back by starvation or disease or war, life was a struggle for existence. Individual variation produced some organisms that were better adapted than others. Only the strongest, best-adapted birds would survive to reproduce.

Darwin was also a disciple of Sir Charles **Lyell** whose geological studies suggested that the Earth was far older than the Bible claimed.

In 1859 Darwin published his book *On the Origin of Species by Natural Selection*. This work aimed to refute the Bible, the first Chapter of Genesis, that all creatures were created by God. Darwin maintained that over millions of years, individual variation could lead to creatures that were better adapted to their environment and would survive, changing imperceptibly over the millennia. What upset people was the concept that the changes were due to entirely random mutation in parents, leading to variation in offspring. This denied the possibility of purpose in evolution and life. The other problem is that induced mutations are almost invariably harmful, in that offspring are less well adapted than their parents.

Darwin's ideas were also held by Alfred Russell **Wallace** (1823–1913) who did his researches in Malaysia. He noticed fundamental differences between the species in Asia and those in Australia, and described *'Wallace's Line'*, between Borneo and Celebes. He wrote to Darwin explaining his belief in Natural Selection, which prompted Darwin to publish his *Origin of Species*. Unfortunately for Wallace, the ship carrying his specimens back to England from South America caught fire and sank and he was unable to mount an exhibition and thereby become famous. It was his correspondence with Darwin that gave urgency to Darwin to publish his seminal work.

Meanwhile, in a monastery in Brünn (now Brno, the capital of the province of Moravia, now part of the Czech Republic) a monk, Gregor **Mendel** (1822–1884) was growing peas. Between 1854 and 1856 he tried 34 varieties of common pea (*Pisum sativum*) before using one that always bred true and had characteristics that were easily identified – short/tall, rough seeds/smooth seeds, green/yellow unripe pod, white/grey seed coat, inflated/constricted seed pod, terminal/axial flower arrangement. Mendel was lucky up to a point because we now know that the pea has seven chromosomes and each trait is located on a different chromosome, so his experiment 'worked'.

He worked with 28,000 plants, 12,835 being studied in detail (these figures are speculative as Mendel's original papers have been lost). He transferred the pollen from one plant to the ovary of another, using a fine brush. The stamens needed to be removed and the ovary carefully covered up to prevent pollination from another plant. In one experiment he crossed a variety with smooth seeds (S) with a variety with rough seeds (r). The next generation were all smooth.

F1 generation - SS x rr = Sr, Sr.Sr Sr.

But in the following (self-fertilised) generation 75% were smooth and 25% rough.

F2 generation - Sr x Sr = SS, Sr rS, rr.

From repeated crosses over 6 generations he concluded that the hereditary factor was a distinct unit which he called Merkmal, which we would now call a *gene* (the term was first used by Wilhelm **Johannsen**, professor of plant physiology at Copenhagen Agricultural College, Denmark, in 1909). Mendel realised that each plant carries two copies (now called allelomorphs or alleles) of the Merkmal, a dominant, a recessive (Mendel's terminology), both or either. In the above experiment, the smooth seeds were dominant, SS, crossed with rough, recessive, rr. First generation hybrids all carried the S Merkmal which was expressed as smooth. But in the second generation, only three out of four carried it. The other one was recessive, rr, and expressed as rough. This 3:1 ratio was the first time that biology had become quantitative, rather than qualitative and descriptive.

Mendel tried to repeat his experiments with the hawkweed, *Hieracium*, but failed. Unfortunately *Heiracium* reproduces asexually, apomixis, (similar to parthenogenesis in certain animals) which would account for his failure.

On 8 February 1865 (with Part 2 in March) Mendel presented his paper to the Brünn Society for the Study of Natural Sciences, summarising eight years of work, to divided but polite reception. Some of the mathematics was quite difficult. The Proceedings of the Society were published in 1866, Mendel requesting 40 reprints. An uncut reprint was found in Charles Darwin's library, so evidently he had not read it. It seems that few read it, or if they did, did not understand its significance.

In 1899, the Dutch botanist Hugo **de Vries** had been doing experiments on hybridization and, 'surveying the literature', to his dismay came across Mendel's paper when he was preparing his own paper for publication, and accepted Mendel's priority in a footnote. This prevented other botanists claiming Mendel's discovery as theirs, thereby avoiding a squabble. He introduced the term 'mutation' (Latin: *mutare* to change) to biology. In England William **Bateson**, having heard de Vries' paper, was an ardent promoter of Mendel's theory. He travelled extensively and coined the word 'genetics' (Greek: γεννειν – to produce) for this new branch of science. He also introduced the F (filial) notation (Latin: *filius* – a son).

From Mendel's experiments two laws were formulated by the German botanist Karl **Correns** in 1900, after Mendel's paper had been rediscovered:

1. Law of Segregation. Hereditary units (genes) occur in pairs. They segregate in the sex cells (gametes), unite in the offspring. Mendel had no idea how this happened. It was not until years later that reduction division, or meiosis, was discovered in the formation of gametes.

2. Law of Independent Assortment. Hereditary units do not blend. But this is not wholly true. Some traits appear to be linked, suggesting that the genes are close to each other on the chromosome.

In a long stay in America, Bateson met Thomas Hunt **Morgan** of Columbia University, the leading researcher in genetics in America. They did not get on. 'T. H. Morgan is a thickhead' he wrote to his sister Beatrice, 'I wish I liked him more'. Morgan thought that Mendel was wrong, but later changed his mind. One thing that they did have in common was rejection of the chromosome theory. Chromosomes (Greek: χρωμα – colour; σωμα – a body) had been seen by several microscopists but were named by the German anatomist **von Waldeyer** in 1888. They take up the stain chromatin during cell division – mitosis – (Greek: μιτοσ – a thread). Walter **Sutton**, a graduate student of Columbia, concluded in 1902: 'The association of maternal and paternal chromosomes in pairs (diploid) and their separation during reduction division (haploid) – meiosis (Greek: μειων – less), may constitute the physical basis of the Mendelian law of heredity'.

Meanwhile, in Germany, Professor Theodor **Boveri** showed that every organism had a specific number of chromosomes – 4 for the roundworm, 32 for the earthworm, 24 for man (actually 23). So the Sutton–Boveri chromosome theory of inheritance became to be generally accepted, but not by Bateson and Morgan. However, two years before his death, Bateson came to accept it: 'I don't like it, but I see no way of escape,' he grumbled.

Back at Columbia, Morgan was looking for a cheap, prolific breeder and chose *Drosophila melanogaster* the banana fruit fly (males have a black abdomen), bred in milk bottles and fed on bananas. In addition, it had four large chromosomes in its salivary glands and reproduces every twelve days. For two years he looked for a mutation in a fly, and finally, in 1910, he noticed a fly with white eyes instead of the usual red (he anaesthetised the flies with ether). He crossed this white-eyed male with a red-eyed female. The white-eyed flies disappeared in the F1 first generation, but reappeared in the second generation in the Mendelian 1:3 ratio. But there were no white-eyed females.

Morgan thought that Mendel was right after all, but in addition he realized that the recessive trait for white eyes was sex linked. The gene for white eyes has to be located on the X chromosome, expressed when there is no balancing gene on the Y male chromosome. This is an example of sex-linked recessive transmission of a trait, transmitted by the female, expressed in the male. Haemophilia is analogous in Man (females have the XX configuration, Males XY in most organisms – in birds and butterflies it is opposite). Sperms either carry the X or Y chromosome, so that sex is determined by the male.

Over the next few years, Morgan, Sturtevant and Bridges used controlled crosses of mutant flies to work out the linear arrangement of genes on the chromosome. In 1925 Herman **Muller** demonstrated the effect of X-rays to induce mutations. Morgan's name is commemorated in the unit of gene separation.

In 1902 the Austrian pathologist Karl **Landsteiner** discovered the blood groups, which he called I, II, III, IV, now called A, B, AB and O. Blood transfusion had been tried, but not always successfully, and Landsteiner discovered why. The A and B factors are present in red blood cells and act as antigens. People can possess either A or B, or both, Group AB, or neither, group O (in London in 1987 about 70% of the population were group O).

In the serum are antibodies designated α and β. A Group A person has β, a group B person has α, a group AB person has neither and a group O person has both. Group O Rh negative is the universal donor. If Group A blood is given to a group B or group O it will agglutinate with the antibody α factor present in the serum and will agglutinate, with disastrous consequences – renal failure.

Hence prior to blood transfusion, donor cells are cross-matched with recipient serum. If agglutination occurs, the blood is incompatible and must not be used. Group AB (a rare group) is the universal recipient as it contains neither the α nor the β factors in the serum. A and B are Mendelian dominants. Blood grouping can be used to exclude paternity, but not to prove it. More recently DNA analysis is used, which can prove it with a high degree of certainty.

In 1937 Landsteiner (now in the USA) and Wiener discovered another blood group known as the Rhesus factor, as it was present in 95% of rhesus monkeys but only 15% of people, who were called rhesus positive. Later the English geneticist R.A. **Fisher** was able to resolve this into the CDE/cde notation. The antigen D is the important one. The significance of this is that if an Rh negative mother has an Rh positive baby or prior transfusion with Rh positive blood, autoimmunisation can occur, with antibodies to D, and the next baby will be born with *erythroblastosis foetalis*, severely anaemic, as the antibodies cross the placenta and haemolyse the blood, or with *hydrops foetalis* which is usually fatal. For many years neonatal exchange transfusion offered the only hope. Nowadays Rh negative mothers are given an injection of anti-D after delivery to prevent the condition arising by eliminating any of the babies' Rh positive red cells which might have entered her circulation.

In Europe and the USA, 85% of the population are Rh positive, but in the Basque country of Spain, uniquely, only 40% are positive, suggesting an unusual origin. Perhaps they are the only survivors of the early Europeans. Asiatics, African Blacks, American Indians and Australian Aborigines are almost entirely Rh positive.

At the beginning of the twentieth century physics, chemistry and biology were distinct disciplines. During this century they had progressively merged and the best example of this was the discovery of the nature and structure of the genetic mechanism, DNA.

In 1953 the English physicist Francis **Crick** and the American biochemist James **Watson**, using X-ray crystallographic evidence from photographs taken by Rosalind **Franklin**, based on ideas of the British biochemist Maurice **Wilkins**, discovered the structure of the molecule of DNA, de-oxy-ribo-nucleic acid. Wilkins, Crick and Watson received the Nobel Prize in 1962, but Rosalind Franklin died in 1958 and the Nobel Prize is never awarded posthumously.

DNA is the principal constituent of the cell nucleus and is responsible for the mechanism of heredity. It consists of a helical structure like a spiral staircase, with the outer rails made of the five-carbon sugar d-ribose, linked by phosphate groups. The rungs of the staircase consist of purine and pyrimidine bases. Adenine links with Thymine, Cytosine with Guanine. Adenine, Thymine, Cytosine and Guanine are called *nucleotides*, when compounded with phosphate and ribose. During cell division (mitosis) the chromosomes migrate to the equator of a spindle and the DNA unwinds. The Adenine/Thymine and Cytosine/Guanine links break (they are held by weak hydrogen bonds) and the two strands fly apart, migrating to the daughter nuclei and at the same time reforming their full complement of nucleotides, and thence further double strands of DNA.

DNA is responsible for the synthesis of proteins. Proteins are made of linked up amino-acids. About 20 different amino-acids have been identified. The simplest amino-acid is glycine – NH_2 – CH_2 – COOH. The NH_2 group is basic, the COOH is acidic. Substitution of one of the hydrogen atoms of the CH_2 group by different groups of molecules gives rise to the other amino-acids. An essential amino acid is one that cannot be synthesised in the body.

The genes are strung out along the chromosomes. The *genotype* is the fundamental hereditary constitution (combination of genes) of an organism. The *phenotype* is the visible appearance of the individual. The *karyotype* is the number, size and shape of the chromosomes in the cell – e.g. trisomy 21 = Down's syndrome: non-disjunction of chromosome 21 leads to 3 instead of 2 chromosomes present in the nucleus (one might hesitantly add – psychotype to describe the non-physical attributes of the individual).

In 1951 the American geneticist Barbara **McClintock**, using maize as her experimental subject, suggested that there were mobile genetic elements that would jump around a chromosome, jumping genes, *transposons*. This work has subsequently been confirmed. The DNA of the Y chromosome and the mitochondrial DNA of the female nucleus do not appear to get 'shuffled' and persist through generations, enabling hereditary traits to be established, useful for anthropologists.

One of the most intriguing aspects of biology is the study of instinctive behaviour. A newly hatched spider is capable of making a perfect web, never having seen one before or having been taught how to make one. Somehow the information is transferred in the DNA of the genome. In Man, instinctive behaviour has been largely replaced by learned behaviour, but a new-born baby instinctively turns its mouth to its mother's breast. Our ignorance of the mechanism of transmission of instinctive behaviour should make one very wary of genetic manipulation.

We, like all living organisms, have been allotted by Inscrutable Fate, or Divine Providence, depending on one's belief, a certain amount of time and a certain amount of space. When we try to increase this space at the expense of others, conflict is inevitable. Birds and other animals have solved this by ritualising conflict so that nobody gets killed. The lamentable history of the twentieth century shows that Man, regrettably and disastrously, has not yet reached this evolutionary advance.

Physics and Chemistry have many Laws. Biology but two:

    1. Adapt or Perish.
    2. Use it or Lose it.

CHAPTER SEVEN

GEOLOGY

To see a World in a Grain of Sand,
and a Heaven in a Wild Flower.,
Hold Infinity in the Palm of your Hand.
Auguries of Innocence
William Blake (1757–1827)

If astronomy is the oldest of sciences, geology, the science of the structure and formation of the Earth, is one of the youngest, barely 200 years old (the Geological Society of London was founded in 1807). A knowledge of the basic scientific disciplines of chemistry physics and biology is necessary to understand geology.

For many years there had been two rival theories with regard to the formation of the Earth. The Vulcanists (Vulcan was the Roman God of Fire) believed that the land arose from volcanic activity, while the Neptunists (Neptune was the Roman God of the Sea) believed that the land arose from disappearance of the sea, in a manner unspecified, perhaps evaporation.

In 1760 the Italian scientist Giovanni **Arduino** proposed that the eras be divided into Primitive (Primary), Secondary and Tertiary. The Secondary era lasted until the chalk formed (Cretaceous), the Tertiary from the Cretaceous until the Ice Age. The Quaternary lasts from the Ice age until the present.

Abraham **Werner** a German mining engineer (1750–1817), the 'father of German geology' taught that there was a succession of rocks, the oldest crystalline rocks such as granite and basalt contained no fossils or evidence of life – Primary. Above these lay the Transition Rocks, such as slates and limestones, with a few fossils. The Secondary period, with stratified sandstones, limestones and gypsum, were filled with fossils. The most recent, Tertiary period were composed of unconsolidated gravels, sand and clay. Werner was a 'Neptunist', a theory subsequently rejected.

The 'father of British geology' – William 'Strata' **Smith** (1769–1839) was a surveyor who was obliged to survey a north Somerset coal mine in 1793. He was impressed by the consistency of the fossils in the various strata as he descended the mine shaft, and identified strata in other areas by their fossil content. He made his first geological map showing the ranges of the different strata in the neighbourhood of Bath, noting their organic remains (fossils) in 1799. Similar fossils were found in strata throughout the country and layers could be traced. With help from Sir Joseph **Banks** (£50), who had supported him throughout, he went on to publish a geological map of England and Wales with part of Scotland in 1815, and in 1831 was awarded a life pension of £100 per annum by the government.

His ideas were based on and supported by the Scottish geologist James **Hutton** (1726–1797) who suggested layering of strata was due to sedimentation, weathering, and consolidation, processes that would have taken millions of years to achieve their present appearances. In 1785 he presented his 'Theory of the Earth' to the Royal Society of Edinburgh.

In later years, Smith fell on hard times, as his stratigraphic map, which brought in some money, had been pirated by the gentlemen of the Geological Society, and he spent some time in a debtor's gaol owing to his inability to repay a mortgage he had taken out on a property in Somerset. He had been forced to sell his collection of 2,657 fossils, together with his 118-page catalogue, for the miserable sum of £500.

Leaving the King's Bench prison, Southwark, in 1819, he boarded the night coach and three days later arrived at Northallerton, Yorkshire, 200 miles from London, together with his unhappy wife, his nineteen-year-old nephew, John Phillips, the tools of his trade – his hammer, theodolite, compass, chain, acid bottle and a few papers – consoling himself with the thought 'When House and Land is gone and spent, then Learning is most excellent.'

He sought occasional work constantly. He was approached by the Corporation of Scarborough to improve its water supply, which he accomplished without difficulty. He gave lectures on geology at a guinea for a series of nine lectures, in York, Leeds, Sheffield and Hull, as well as Scarborough, where he helped design and set up the City Museum. This was a Rotunda, a circular structure with Doric columns. Here fossils were exhibited in chronological order so that the most primitive fossils (triassic) were at the bottom of a spiral, most recent (Cretaceous) at the top, and at the time people flocked to see it.

Smith had met the MP for Scarborough Sir John Vanden Bempde **Johnston** at meetings of the Philosophical Society of Scarborough, and in 1828 he was hired as Land Steward to Sir John, at the village of Hackness, in the valley of the Derwent, about six miles from Scarborough, and gave him use of a vicarage. Thus his situation became known and numerous friends of geology came to visit. One of these was William **Vernon**, a Derbyshire chemist and lens maker. Vernon was distressed to see the old man (he was then 58) in somewhat reduced circumstances and wrote to Sir Roderick **Murchison** (the Scottish soldier, explorer, geologist and founder of the Silurian period) and to Adam **Sedgwick**, co-founder of the Devonian, suggesting that Smith should receive the honour due to him, a subscription raised for the purchase of an annuity, and to prevent him dying in the Poor House.

Four years were to elapse before Sedgwick became President of the Geological Society and the matter could be addressed. In 1828 William Hyde **Wollaston** died, bequeathing £1000 to establish a fund to provide a medal and an award each year to the person for his or her research into 'the mineral structure of the Earth.' He was a doctor, a chemist, had discovered palladium, and made a fortune from ways of working with platinum. The Wollaston Medal is the Nobel Prize for geology.

On 11 January 1831 a formal resolution was passed at a special meeting of the council of the Geological Society that the first ever Wollaston Medal should be awarded to William Smith, and that he should be granted the proceeds of the Wollaston Fund. Those present at this meeting included William

Broderick, Rev William Whewell, Leonard Horner, Dr Peter Roget (who wrote the *Thesaurus*), Capt James Vetch, Henry de la Beche (first head of the Geological Survey), Prof. Edward Turner, Roderick Murchison, and John Taylor (William Herschel was also a member but was not present on that occasion).

The news was conveyed to Smith at Harkness and on 18 February he presented himself at the Society's anniversary. 'At their meeting every countenance glowed with delight,' Smith wrote to his niece, Ann, 'when the twenty guinea purse was delivered to me... then ninety merry philosophical faces glowed over a most sumptuous dinner at the Crown and Anchor.'

Further honours were to follow. In 1832 he received the Wollaston Medal, which had now been made of gold, and engraved, at the Sheldonian Theatre in Oxford. A panel of scientists had petitioned the king, William IV, and Smith was granted a pension of £100 a year, deemed adequate to keep the wolf from the door, and to continue to support his widow, Mary Ann, who died five years after him, in York asylum. A visiting friend described her a being 'very cheerful, made the whole company laugh.'

He was further honoured when the British Association for the Advancement of Science was meeting in Dublin. There he was given an honorary Doctorate of Letters.

In 1834 the Palace of Westminster, where Parliament meets, had been destroyed by fire and a committee was set up to advise on it's rebuilding. This included Sir Charles Barry, his son Edward, and August Pugin. Dr William Smith was asked to advise on the type of stone to be used. Unfortunately the gloomy Permian limestone chosen could not stand up to the foul acidic atmosphere of London at the time, and ten years later it all had to be replaced with the warm honey-coloured Middle Jurassic oolitic stone of Lincolnshore, the Clipsham Stone. Smith seems to have escaped the opprobrium due to the committee's error of judgement.

In 1834 Smith moved back to live in Scarborough, and rented, for £15 a year, a small house in Bar Street called Newborough Cottage. On returning from a meeting of the British Association in Birmingham, he fell ill at Northampton and died on 28 August. He was buried nearby, in St Peters Church.

His nephew, John **Phillips**, who became Professor of Geology at Oxford University, in 1841 suggested that the old divisions Primary, Transition, Secondary and Tertiary eras should be replaced by terms that reflected the fossil evidence. Primary became *Azoic* (no life), Transition became *Palaezoic* (ancient Life), Secondary became *Mesozoic* (middle life – contained fossil reptiles), Tertiary became *Cenozoic* (newer forms of life).

It was Sir Charles **Lyell** (1797–1875) who put geology on a firmer foundation by suggesting the principle of Unitarianism, that geological processes continue at a uniform rate, that the Earth must have evolved through millions of years. From 1830 to 1833 he wrote in three volumes *The Principles of Geology*, which went into twelve editions. He devised the classification universally accepted – *Eocene* (dawn of recent), *Miocene* (less of recent) and *Pliocene* (more of recent). His unitarianism principle was in opposition to the Catastrophists, who believed that sudden changes, such as Noah's Flood, accounted for the appearance of various animals and plants. Darwin's Theory of Evolution by Natural Selection had been based on Lyell's ideas.

In 1912 the German meteorologist Alfred **Wegener** (1880–1930) introduced his theory of continental drift, to widespread ridicule, that the land masses are not fixed but slowly move about, a theory now fully accepted and known as *Plate Tectonics*. Earthquakes, which occur at tectonic plate boundaries, and the formation of mountains can be explained by this theory. Wegener did not live to see his theory vindicated.

According to present theory, about 250 million years ago there was but one supercontinent, *Pangea*, that stretched from pole to pole. About 200 million years ago, this split up into a northern half, *Laurasia* and a southern half, *Gondwana* (accurate Global Positioning System measurement suggests that Europe and North America are moving apart at a rate of about 10 centimetres a year). The plates that carry the land masses are about 20 kilometres thick, while the oceanic plates are about 7 kilometres thick. When a plate meets another one, it is pushed down, a process known as *subduction*, causing an earth-quake. The strength of earthquakes is measured in the *Richter Scale*, an open-ended logarithmic scale where the most massive earthquake would be 9.5. The earthquake that destroyed San Francisco in 1906 was 8.3. Scale of 1 would only be detected by very sensitive seismographs. 2 would be 10 times more power-ful, 3 would be 100 times more powerful, and so on.

Rocks are the solid materials of the outer Earth.

Minerals are naturally occurring inorganic crystalline solids, comprising various chemical elements.

Rocks are classified as:
1. *Igneous*, having been formed from a liquid magma deep in the Earth or extruded on to the surface by volcanoes. They are further classified as *intrusive*, formed beneath the Earth's surface (e.g. granite) and *extrusive*, formed from molten material forced to the Earth's surface (lava, basalt).

2. *Sedimentary*, having been formed by the accumulation of sediment in water and air and by the processes of ero-sion, precipitation, evaporation and compaction.

3. *Metamorphic*, rocks changed by varying degrees of heat and pressure on any type of existing rock.

Igneous rocks include:
Granite consists of quartz, feldspar and mica.
Quartz is silica, silicon dioxide, SiO_2. Clear quartz is rock crystal. Purple quartz is amethyst. Its melting point is about 1710^0C. It is piezo-electric in that its edges develop electric charges when subject to pressure. Thin slices are used in oscil-lators and clocks as electric resonators, the frequency being determined by the thickness of the slice. It crystallizes in the hexagonal rhombohedral system. There are six basic crystal systems – Cubic, Tetragonal, Hexagonal, Orthorhombic, Monoclinic, and Triclinic.

Feldspar comprises 50% of the Earth's crust., and is five times more common than quartz. Two types are described. Orthoclase, which is potassium aluminium silicate, and plagioclase, which is sodium calcium aluminium silicate. Feldspar weathers to kaolin (china clay.) Orthoclase feldspars are often pink-coloured due to iron content.

Biotite *mica* is a complex silicate of potassium, aluminium, magnesium and iron. In granite it is black. It is a poor conductor of heat and electricity and is used as an insulator and, by virtue of its ability to form large sheets, as an alternative to glass, which is a silicate of sodium, potassium or calcium.

Igneous rocks have been classified by their silica content. Granite is an acidic rock, containing more than 63% silica, Basalt is basic, containing between 45 and 52% silica.

Basalt (found also in Moon rock and meteorites) is black and fine grained due to rapid cooling: slow cooling – 100,000 years, leads to large crystals. Basic volcanic rock consisting of olivine, which is green (a silicate of iron and magnesium) and pyroxene, which a complex silicate of sodium, calcium, aluminium, with iron, magnesium, nickel or lithium, Augite, feldspar and silica.

Sedimentary rocks include:

Sandstones, composed of quartz grains cemented with silica, lime or iron oxides.

Shales and *mudstones,* are formed from clays that have hardened into rock.

Limestones consist of calcite (calcium carbonate – $CaCO_3$) formed from the shells and remains of dead organisms and ooliths.

Flints or *cherts* are classified as sedimentary and are formed from silica. They only occur in association with chalk or limestone and one possible theory to account for their curious shape (they are nearly always covered with a white cortex of calcium carbonate) and distribution suggests they were formed from solidified colloidal silica in burrows of sea-creatures such as crustacea. At any rate they are extremely hard and fracture like glass in a conchoidal manner leaving an extremely sharp edge. They played an important part in the ascent of Man in that

Stone Age man made use of them as knives, spear heads and arrowheads, thus providing food, clothing and shelter.

Metamorphic rocks include:
Slate, formed from shale.
Marble, formed from limestone.
Quartzite, formed from sandstone.
Anthracite, a hard coal formed from a soft coal.

Rocks and minerals are further classified according to size of particle:
1. Clay – diameter less than 4 microns (0.004 millimetres)
2. Silt – diameter between 4 and 62 microns.
3. Sand – diameter between 62 microns and 2 millimetres.
4. Granule – diameter between 2 and 4 millimetres (quarter of an inch).
5. Pebble – diameter between 4 and 64 millimetres (2 inches).
6. Cobble – diameter between 64 millimetres and 256 millimetres (10 inches)
7. Boulder – diameter larger than 256 millimetres.

Rocks and Minerals are described according to their physical properties.

1. Density, (mass per unit volume) or specific gravity – weight of the substance compared with an equal volume of water.

2. Hardness – Mohs' scale. The German mineralogist Friedrich **Mohs** (1773–1839) classified the hardness of rocks from the softest – talc 1 (soapstone, hydrated magnesium silicate) to the hardest – 10 (diamond, crystalline carbon). A high number will scratch a lower number.

3. Cleavage. The property of some minerals to break along planes related to the molecular structure of the mineral, and parallel to actual or possible crystal faces.
Several crystal systems are described.

i.   Cubic, such as common salt, (halite, sodium chloride, NaCe) and galena, lead sulphide (PbS).
ii. Tetragonal
iii. Hexagonal, such as beryl, emerald, (beryllium aluminium silicate), quartz (silicon dioxide)
iv   Rhombohedral, such as calcite (Calcium Carbonate $CaCO_3$).
v.   Orthorhombic,
vi. Monoclinic.
vii. Triclinic.
viii. Basal, such as mica.

4. Fracture. Minerals that do not cleave easily fracture irregularly. Fractures are described as conchoidal (shell-like, such as glass, obsidian and quartz and flints): hackly (metals and tough minerals like jade) and earthy, like clay and chalk.

5. Other properties include Colour, lustre, transparency, fluorescence, magnetism and radioactivity.

Palaeontology is the study of fossils.

Fossils are the preserved remains of once living creatures. They may be preserved by *incrustation* or *petrification*, and are found in sedimentary rocks (limestones and shales). In incrustation the outline of the bacterium, fungus plant or animal is preserved as sediments are deposited around it. In petrification, mineralisation occurs, the carbon atom of the organism being replaced by a silicon atom (both are tetravalent). Sometimes the atom is one of iron. Conditions must have been such as to prevent decay of the organism, by excluding oxygen. To be considered a fossil, the remains must be more than 10,000 years old.

Fossils are also classified as animal, plant or trace.

Index fossils represent a species that was once widespread geographically but only existed for a brief period, mainly marine creatures, of which *ammonites* are one of the best known, are the index or zone fossil for the Jurassic period.

The discovery of the *dinosaurs* is one of the most intriguing. Fossil ammonites had been found at Lyme Regis in Dorset along the South Coast of England for years. They were so called because they resembled Ammon, the horn of the Roman God Jupiter. Or possibly Amun-Ra, the ancient Egyptian god, 2,500BC. They were also known as snake stones, from their coiled appearance. At any rate they were credited with magical properties, being alleged cures for blindness, impotence, and barrenness.

During the early part of the nineteenth century a young teenager, Mary **Anning**, collected them from the beach at Lyme Regis and sold them. The family had fallen on hard times as her carpenter father had died following an accident. She sold one particularly attractive fossil for the sum of two shillings and six-pence, enough to feed the family for a week.

Ammonites were creatures that we now know lived during the Carboniferous period, about 300 million years ago and were extinct by the Cretaceous, about 150 million years ago. They were cephalopods (the Octopus is a cephalopod, having its legs attached to its head). A stratum of blue lias, containing fossils, reaches the surface at Lyme Regis, and rock falls in this unstable area reveal fossils.

At the end of the eighteenth century, with the Industrial Revolution, much excavation was going on, to dig mines for coal and minerals, to dig canals for transport and for materials for housing, as with increasing urbanisation, farming jobs were replaced by factory jobs. This activity brought to light many curious objects whose nature and origin remained obscure.

In 1811, Joseph Anning, Mary's brother, discovered a giant fossilised creature rather like a crocodile, 4 feet long. A year later, Mary found an even larger fossil, 17 feet long, which she sold to the local Lord of the Manor for £23, enough to feed the family for six months. It had a head similar to a crocodile with sharp interlocking teeth, enormous bony eye sockets, sixty ver-tebrae, some 3 inches across, and flippers, similar to a fish. It was put on display in Piccadilly and quite baffled the scientists of the day. It was named *Icthyosaurus* (fish-lizard) by Charles **Konig**, Keeper of Natural History at the British Museum, where it was subsequently placed.

In 1991 the archaeologist Keary **Walde** discovered the fossilised remains of a giant Icthyosaur beside the Sikanni Chief River in northern British Columbia, Canada, embedded in limestone. It was 23 metres (75 feet) long and its skull was 5.8 metres (19 feet) long. It was the largest marine reptile known, and lived in the Triassic age, between 210 and 220 million years ago. The largest animal ever is the Blue Whale, 200 tons, 33 metres long.

In 1821 Mary Mantell, wife of a local doctor Gideon **Mantell**, picked up a curious object at a quarry at Cuckfied, West Sussex. Dr Mantell, the son of a shoemaker, had been fascinated by fossils since a young boy, and qualified as a doctor in order to make a living. He had a thriving practice in Lewes, and spent most of his spare time searching for and examining fossils. Dr Mantell had found the fossilised remains of enormous bones at the quarry, unlike anything previous known, and realised that this object was a giant tooth. But it did not have the sharp pointed crown of the carnivore and was more like the tooth of a herbivore, with a flattened grinding surface. Yet it was present in ancient strata, deeper than any mammalian remains, and so was unlikely to belong to a hippopotamus or rhinoceros. Preposterously, it must have come from a giant herbivorous lizard. Yet there were the remains of a thigh bone, 30 inches long and 25 inches in circumference, scaled up, the animal would have to be 40 feet long – impossible!

But such bones had already been dug up at Oxfordshire, and had been residing at the Ashmoleum Museum in Oxford for well over a century. They had been described in 1677 by Dr Robert **Plot**, who thought they must have come from an elephant, brought over by the Roman legions. Further bones were found in a quarry at Stonesfield, near Woodstock.

Rev. William **Buckland** had been appointed Reader in Geology at Oxford University and Professor of Geology in 1818, his stipend having been approved by the Treasury at the request of the Prince Regent, subsequently George IV. He invited Baron Georges **Cuvier** from the Paris Natural History Museum, to see the bones and identify them. Cuvier was considered the foremost expert in fossils as he had identified fossil mastodons and mammoths, whose remains had been found in the permafrost in Siberia. But Cuvier was as baffled as the rest, though he thought they must have come from a reptile rather than a mammal as teeth were found characteristic of reptiles having young teeth formed within the cavity of older teeth.

Buckland was reluctant to publish his views, being a priest of the Church. The problem was that the teaching of the Bible was sacrosanct, yet geological evidence suggested that the strata had been laid down not in centuries or millennia but millions if not hundreds of millions of years ago, quite contradicting the Bible, which claimed the Earth was but 7,000 years old. Changes were attributed to Noah's Flood.

In May 1822, Dr Mantell published his book *Fossils of the South Downs*, giving a fairly accurate description of what was subsequently known as a dinosaur. In 1822 he took some of his fossil teeth to a meeting of the Geological Society in London, but the experts, Rev. Buckland and Rev. **Conybeare**, founder members of the society, were not impressed, believing the fossils were in a more recent stratum. However, together with Charles Lyell, Mantell identified other strata confirming his original belief. Still his views were rejected by the Geological Society. The problem was that Dr Mantell was not regarded as a serious investigator, a mere amateur.

In 1823 Dr Mantell took his fossil tooth to Baron Cuvier in Paris. Perhaps guided by Rev. Buckland, Cuvier was not impressed, saying it was the tooth of a hippopotamus, disregarding the stratigraphic evidence.

Later that year, Mary Anning unearthed another giant fossil under the Black Ven at Lyme Regis. It was 9 feet long, with a tiny head and a huge neck with a spine of 90 vertebrae. It had paddles like a fish. It was named by Rev. Conybeare *Pleisosaurus* – 'near to reptile'. Cuvier, however thought it was a forgery. He considered it impossible for a creature to have 35 cervical (neck) vertebrae. Mammals generally have 7, birds from 9 to 23, reptiles from 3 to 8. However Charles Konig at the British Museum was convinced of its authenticity. It was presented at a meeting of the Geological Society on 20 February 1824, having been transported to London with great difficulty.

It would not go upstairs into the lecture room and the various members had to go down to the entrance passage to see it, and were duly amazed. Mary Anning's reputation as a fossil hunter was assured. At this meeting, Rev. William Buckland at last presented his fossils from the Oxford Stonesfield site, naming his animal Megalosaurus. Later that year Dr Mantell sent further teeth to Baron Cuvier, who relented and admitted that they came from an unknown animal.

Then Dr Mantell had a bit of luck. He went to London and met William **Clift**, Curator of the Hunterian Museum of the Royal College of Surgeons of England and, by chance, Samuel **Sutchbury**, assistant curator, was there having just returned from Barbados in the West Indies bringing with him a specimen of an iguana. Mantells' fossils bore a remarkable similarity to the bony structure, particularly the jaws and teeth, to the iguana, scaled up 20 times or more. Mantell suggested the name Iguanasaurus for his creature, but Rev. Conybeare thought that Iguanodon was more appropriate, meaning 'Tooth of iguana'. Iguanasaurus meant iguana lizard, inappropriately. Even Baron Cuvier was won over, to everyone's satisfaction, and Dr Mantell's fame seemed assured, and he wished to present a paper to the Royal Society, the oldest and most prestigious scientific Society in England (founded in 1660 with the approval of Charles II, receiving its Royal Charter in 1663). Dr Mantell's paper was read by Davies Gilbert, Esq.

Dr Mantell was now accepted as a proper scientist and was elected a member of the Council of the Geological Society and later, a Fellow of the Royal Society, the greatest accolade that could be bestowed upon him, a shoemaker's son and a country doctor. It was indeed a remarkable achievement, to postulate the previous existence of a giant herbivorous lizard from a single tooth, all from a knowledge of comparative anatomy and stratigraphy.

In 1827 Dr Mantell published his researches *Illustrations of the Geology of Sussex*, but it did not receive much interest and only 150 copies were printed, 50 were sold. In 1833, with £1000 patronage from Lord Egremont, he sold his medical practice in Lewes and moved to Brighton, which had become fashionable since the Prince Regent, now George IV, had built his remarkable Pavilion. He signed a lease on 20 Old Steyne, an elegant house, barely 100 yards from the Pavilion, where he set up a museum on the ground floor and lectured about his fossils. Initially it was a great success 'hundreds of the nobility and gentry flocked through the door'. In 1835 Dr Mantell was presented with the Wollaston Medal of the Geological Society by Charles Lyell, now President of the Society. This accolade was a high point in his career.

But without his medical practice money was becoming short. He was forced to give up the lease on his house and to turn it into a museum, 'The Sussex Scientific Institution and Mantellian Museum', with 30,000 specimens (estimated) – with a room for him on the top floor. His wife and four children were to be placed in lodgings. Mrs Mantell was furious that his obsession with fossils had led to the family's eviction, and moved back to Lewes, to a modest cottage at the bottom of a hill from which she could see her old home, Castle Place, never to return to him.

Perhaps Dr Mantell should have rested on his laurels, as the rest of life can only be described as decline and fall. At least he admitted 'In truth, I am now sick of the cold-blooded creatures I am surrounded by.' He gave his last lecture on 21 October 1837. His patron Lord Egremont had died and he was forced to sell his collection of fossils. After protracted negotiations, he was offered £4,087 by the British Museum. 'What a lesson in humility, what a proof of the vanity of human expectation' he wrote in his diary.

Dr Mantell moved to Clapham, South London, to try to establish a practice there, in 1839. His wife had deserted him, his son Walter, trained as a surgeon, emigrated to New Zealand, against his father's wishes. His daughter Ellen had left, his son Reginald was training to be an engineer, he was alone except for his 'sweet girl', his daughter Hannah. But Hannah was seriously ill with tuberculous osteomyelitis of the hip. After three years of ill health, Hannah died from a haemorrhage and her father was desolate.

In 1837 Queen Victoria ascended the throne and the scientific spotlight fell on Richard **Owen**, who spoke French. His mother was of French descent and he had ingratiated himself with Baron Cuvier on a visit of the latter to England. Owen was assistant curator of the Hunterian Museum of the Royal College of Surgeons of England and was asked by the British Association for the Advancement of Science (BA) to 'Report on the present state of knowledge of the Fossil Reptiles of Great Britain.'

In 1841 Owen was fortunate in that a fossil sacrum from an Iguanodon had been found, which had 5 fused vertebrae, similar to man, and this gave evidence that the animal walked upright, and lived on land. With the assistance of others, he coined the name *dinosauria*, deinos (Greek: δεινοσ – terrible, or fearfully great), and sauros, (σαυροσ – a lizard) for a distinct tribe or sub-order. He gave no credit to Dr Mantell for the work that he had done earlier, motivated by hostility and jealousy (it's not love but jealousy that makes the world go round).

On 11 October 1841, Dr Mantell, on his rounds, had an unfortunate accident. His carriage, going too fast along Clapham Common, turned over and he was flung to the ground and he suffered several fractured lumbar vertebrae. He was paralysed and in severe pain and unable to resume his medical work. By 1844 his daughter Ellen had returned to him and helped him with his geological work. He published another book, *Medals of Creation*, which was a success.

His son Walter, whom he had not seen for eight years, having left for New Zealand in September 1839, sent him a box of 800 fossils in December 1847. He had earlier written to his father saying that he was penniless and destitute, and his father had sent him money and urged him to return. The fossils contained those of a large flightless bird, the *moa* or *dinornis*, which could attain a height of 12 feet. This creature had previously been postulated by Owen from fossils he had received in 1839, and in spite of their cool relationship, Dr Mantell invited Owen to see them.

Walter obtained a position as Commissioner for the Purchase of Lands by the Governor of New Zealand and set out to catch a moa, as he thought there might be a living descendant.

Meanwhile Dr Mantell's youngest son Reginald had returned from America and was working as an engineer on the construction of the Great Western Railway, under I. K. Brunel. On the section between Chippenham and Trowbridge he unearthed superb specimens of fossil **belemnites** (an extinct mollusc related to the squid and cuttlefish). There had been early controversy over these, as Owen had presented a paper and received a Gold Medal from the Royal Society for his work on them, entirely disregarding work that had been done earlier by an amateur geologist, Chaning **Pearce**. Reginald showed the fossils to his father, who presented a paper to the Royal Society in 1848. This showed that Owen had not got priority and further that his anatomical description was incorrect.

In 1849 Dr Mantell received a fossil tibia 58 inches in circumference, found at Malling Hill near Lewes. A further find was a humerus $4^1/_2$ feet long (bought for £8), which meant the animal was about 80 feet long, the largest creature to have walked on the face of the Earth. Dr Mantell called it a **Pelorosaurus** (Greek: πελορ – monster). It belonged to the family of sauropods – 'lizard foot', which includes **Brontosaurus**, **Diplodocus** and **Apatosaurus**.

In November 1849 his name was again proposed for the prestigious Royal Medal of the Royal Society and, supported by Sir Charles Lyell and Rev. Buckland, it was awarded, on 30 November, opposed by Professor Owen. Further evidence of Owen's duplicity was his attempt to pass off some of Dr Mantell's plates of fossil drawings, as his own, in 1842, when in fact they were done by Dr Mantell in 1841.

All the speculation as to the anatomy of the dinosaurs was confirmed when a dinosaur graveyard was discovered in 1878, at Bernissart in Belgium. Coal miners were drilling more than 1000 feet underground when they came across huge bones. An entire skeleton was unearthed. In fact 31 skeletons of Iguanodon were found, whose length varied from 13 to 30 feet in length.

On 1 May 1851 the Great Exhibition was opened in Hyde Park. Joseph Paxton's glittering Crystal Palace covered nearly twenty acres. There were eleven miles of stands, devoted to art, science, and human ingenuity. Richard Owen served on its committee, saw to the arrangements, which brought him into close contact with the Royal family. Dr Mantell managed to visit the Exhibition several times, in spite of the severe pain that his back injury was causing.

In the summer of 1852 the Crystal Palace Company aimed to relocate the Great Exhibition in 200 acres of landscaped ground at Penge Hill, Sydenham, South London. Dr Mantell was approached to supervise the arrangement of a 'Geological Court', recognition at last. But it was not to be. His health was now so bad that he could not undertake the task, which meant a year's work. Earl **Rosse**, President of the Royal Society, recognising his plight, made arrangements for the Queen to give him a Civil List grant of £100 a year. He needed huge amounts of laudanum (*Tinct opii*) to ease his pain.

On 10 November 1852, he died following a fall, and was buried at Norwood Cemetery, next to his 'beloved child' Hannah Matilda. A post-mortem showed that the deformity of his spine meant that some of his lower lumbar vertebrae were at right angles to their proper position, the intervertebral discs had disintegrated. Ironically, this specimen was placed in Professor Owen's museum at the Royal College of Surgeons of England at Lincoln's Inn Fields, London, only to be lost when a bomb fell on the College at the height of the blitz in 1941.

In 1856 Reginald Mantell died in India, of cholera, while working on engineering projects, aged 30, and was buried at Allahabad. On hearing the news, Walter sailed to England, and, with Sir Charles Lyell's help, returned to New Zealand with many prized fossil specimens, including the tooth which had led to the discovery of Iguanodon. Walter Mantell helped to found a scientific society in New Zealand, which became the Royal Society of New Zealand.

By virtue of his Royal connections Owen was able to oversee his grand project, the building of the Natural History Museum, opened in 1880 at South Kensington, where his statue greets the visitor. By this time Owen was an old man but he had seen to it that very little of Mantell's collection of fossils was exhibited in the museum.

In 1859 Charles Darwin published his *Origin of Species*, and created a sensation throughout society, disputing the truth of the Bible and its description of the origin of mankind. This work encapsulated the thoughts and feelings of many eminent men at the time, but it was regarded as heretical, and people had been burnt at the stake centuries before for such heresy. It threatened the entire social structure of England, which had been described by Charles Lyell as 'the most Parson-ridden country in Europe apart from Spain'.

Owen was on the side of the 'creationists' and was opposed by the 'evolutionists' especially the geologist Thomas Henry **Huxley**, a lecturer at the Government Department of Mines. Matters came to a head at a debate in Oxford, the home of the clergy, on Saturday, 30 June 1860. Advised by Owen, the Bishop of Oxford, Dr Samuel Wilberforce ('Soapy Sam' – the son of William Wilberforce who did much to promote the abolition of the slave trade), was pitched against Huxley.

Wilberforce, at the end of his oration, turned to Huxley and uttered the ultimate insult, 'he begged to know, was it through his grandfather or his grandmother that he claimed descent from a monkey?' At that, Huxley, who was somewhat outspoken, emphatically striking his hand upon his knee, exclaimed 'I would rather be descended from an ape than from a bishop.' Great consternation. Lady Brewster swooned and had to be carried out. One can insult a scientist with impunity, but to insult a Man of the Cloth in public is the ultimate solecism. It probably cost Huxley a knighthood. He later wrote that he would not be ashamed to have a monkey for an ancestor, but he would be ashamed to be connected with a man who used great gifts to obscure the truth. This event marked the breakdown in relations between Science and Religion.

• • • •

The Earth's history after 570MYBP (million years before the present) is divided into eras, periods and epochs. Prior to this is

Precambrian time. The earliest fossils are **stromatolites**, produced by algae and cyanobacteria, about 3.5BYBP (billion years before the present). They probably started the conversion of the primitive Earth's atmosphere from carbon dioxide and nitrogen to oxygen and nitrogen. They can be found at Shark Bay, Western Australia.

The **Paleozoic Era** started about 570 million years ago and lasted 375 million years. The names of each period are derived from areas where fossils were found. The Cambrian Mountains are in Wales. Other names are derived from tribes that once lived in the area. They include:

CAMBRIAN PERIOD – Animal life was entirely marine, **trilobites** (a primitive arthropod), molluscs, snails foraminifera, seaweeds, bryozoans. Lichens appeared on land. At the end of this time the trilobites were extinct.

ORDOVICIAN PERIOD – started 500 million years ago, characterised by **graptolites** (primitive chordates), primitive fish and **corals**.

SILURIAN PERIOD – started 430 million years ago. First air breathing animal appeared, a scorpion. Also vascular plants appeared.

DEVONIAN PERIOD – started 395 million years ago. Woody plants ferns and rushes appeared. Petrified stumps of trees up to 60cm diameter have been found. Sharks, lungfish starfish and sponges were present.

CARBONIFEROUS PERIOD – started 345 million years ago. Amphibians reptiles, spiders and insects appeared. Cockroaches and a huge dragonfly-like insect with a wingspan of 74cm has been found. But the principal finding of this period was the development of the forests of huge trees (scale trees) 30 metres high and 1.8m in diameter, and the first conifers appeared. This period was when the coal fields were formed, hence the name.

PERMIAN PERIOD – began 280 million years ago. Many marine animals became extinct and reptiles appeared. Vegetation consisted of ferns and conifers.

The **Mesozoic Era** began 225 million years ago and lasted 160 million years. The age of the reptiles. It includes:

TRIASSIC PERIOD – Ammonites and sea urchins have been found

but this was the beginning of the age of the dinosaurs, *icthyosaurs* and early flying reptiles, *pterosaurs*. In the sea the early bony fish the teleosts appear. On land, early mammals and predominant trees gingkos, palms and conifers appear.

JURASSIC PERIOD – began about 195 million years ago. Dinosaurs dominated this period. They grew ever more massive, and winged reptiles, the pterodactyls, some with wingspans as much as 1.2 metres, appeared. In the sea were found *plesiosaurs* (a group that had broad flat bodies like turtles with large flippers for swimming and long necks), icthyosaurs, and primitive *crocodiles* (the famous Loch Ness Monster, whose existence has yet to be confirmed, and whose appearance may well be related to the consumption of a local beverage, has been thought to have been a plesiosaur). This was a mild period, and plant life flourished, dominated by cycads. Many insects appeared, moths, flies, beetles, grasshoppers and termites. Four orders of small mammals appeared, smaller than dogs.

CRETACEOUS PERIOD – began 136 million years ago. Reptiles predominated, dinosaurs, snakes and lizards. Fossil pterodactyls have been found in Texas with wingspans of 15.5 metres (50 feet). Marsupials developed and the first placental mammals made their appearance. But the most important advance was in the plant kingdom, with the appearance of angiosperms – flowering plants. Most of the modern trees had made their appearance by the end of the period, including magnolia, fig, poplar, beech, walnut, holly, maple, oak laurel and plane trees (fossil pollen confirms this). The period is remarkable for the huge deposits of chalk and limestone (varieties of calcium carbonate), formed from the shells of microscopic marine animals, that occurred in this period. Chalk and limestone are sedimentary deposits rich in fossils in certain areas. At the end of the Cretaceous about 65MYBP there was a mass extinction, probably due to an asteroid colliding with the Earth in the region of the Gulf of Mexico, with the dust thrown up obscuring the sunlight leading to destruction of the vegetation on which most life depended. The dinosaurs were wiped out. This has been called the K–T boundary, between Cretaceaous and Tertiary.The

Cenozoic Era began 65 Million Years ago. Most of the large reptiles had gone and mammals dominated.

The *Paleocene epoch* lasted about 11 million years. Primitive bear-like mammals appeared, now extinct. Groups that have survived include the marsupials, the primates, the insectivores, and the rodents,

The *Eocene epoch* began about 54 million years ago. Ancestors of modern animals appeared, including small horses (eohippus), camels, monkeys, aquatic mammals, eagles, pelicans, vultures.

The *Oligocene epoch* began about 38 million years ago and modern mammals began to appear such as anthropoid apes and carnivores similar to cats and dogs.

The *Miocene epoch* began 26 million years ago. The grasses appeared (grasses grow from the base rather than the tip, so they are not killed by being eaten). This led to the development of grazing animals such as cows, horses, camels, and rhinoceroses and the mastodon evolved.

The *Pliocene epoch* began 12 million years ago with little difference from the miocene.

The *Pleistocene epoch* was characterised by the development of the large mammals. Mastodons and mammoths, and the giant sabre-toothed tiger became extinct. Modern Man appeared.

The *Holocene epoch* is the most recent, the last 10,000 years, the upper part of the Quaternary Period.*

Dating Techniques

The age of the Earth has been for many years a matter of speculation. About 1654 James Usher, Archbishop of Armagh, Primate of Ireland, declared that God had created the Earth on 23 October 4004bc, basing his calculations on the Tables of Genealogy in the Bible (Methuselah lived to be 969 according to

---

*A useful mnemonic (a phrase, usually of a humorous or obscene nature devised with a view to assisting the memory of a sequence) helps to place these periods: Camels Often Sit Down Carefully, Perhaps Their Joints Creak. Early Oiling May Prove Positively Helpful (also useful for the geological timetable).

Genesis V v.29. However in 1997 the oldest authenticated person was Mme Jeanne Calment who died at Arles, France, in 1997 aged 122 – 'God has forgotten me' she said).

Rings on trees and stalactites can give more scientific estimates of recent events, thickness of sedimentary rocks has been used, but radioactive dating is generally used today. The principles of this are as follows. Isotopes of many elements breakdown over a period of time in a constant manner. Half of the mass of an element goes constantly, known as the half-life. The rate of decay is independent of environmental factors such as temperature or pressure and can be accurately measured. The ratio of decayed element to parent element is a measure of the age of the substance under consideration. Uranium 238 decays through 5 disintegrations to lead 206, its half life being 4.51 billion years. The oldest Earth rock has been dated at about 3.8 billion years, suggesting that the Earth had a solid crust at that time, but Moon rock and meteorites (originating in the asteroid belt) have been dated at 4.6 billion years, suggesting that the solar system began about then.

Radiocarbon dating is a technique that was developed by the American scientist W.F. **Libby** (1908–1980) about 1946. It is useful for rocks that contain wood fragments and are less than 70,000 years old. Plants absorb carbon from the atmosphere in the form of carbon dioxide, and when the plant dies no further uptake occurs. Most of the carbon in the atmosphere is C^{12}, but a small proportion is the radioactive C^{14}, produced from neutron bombardment of atmospheric nitrogen. It has a half life of 5,730±40 years and decays to N^{14}. The ratio of C^{14} to N^{14} gives the age of the specimen. A possible source of error is the uncertainty of the proportion of C^{14} present in the atmosphere at the time the plant was living, it is only present today at about one part per million. However confirmation and calibration has been provided by measuring the annual rings of the bristle-cone pine trees of California, at 6000 years the oldest living organisms. Their habitat at an elevation of 11,000 feet prevents biological decay.

CHAPTER EIGHT

THE NOBEL PRIZE

ALFRED NOBEL (1833–1896)

Alfred was the third son of an explosive manufacturer, Immanuel Nobel, who was commissioned by the Russian Government to make submarine mines for the defence of the Crimea. For a time Immanuel lived in St Petersburg but the Russians reneged on his contract and, bankrupted, he moved back to Stockholm, where his wife and family lived.

Alfred was born on 21 October 1833. He received little formal education and was taught by a private tutor, like his brothers, until he was sixteen. But by then he was a remarkable linguist, who knew English, German, French and Russian as well as Swedish, and was a scientifically trained chemist.

At that time his father's business was prospering and he travelled abroad for two years, visiting America but spending most of his time in Paris, where he continued his studies in Chemistry.

In October 1863 he obtained his first patent in Sweden for a percussion detonator called the 'Nobel Lighter'.

In September 1864 an explosion in the Nobel factory, which manufactured the highly unstable nitroglycerine (glycerol trinitrate), killed three employees including his younger brother Emil. Alfred sought a way of stabilising nitroglycerine, the basis of the explosive. He found this could be done by absorbing it in a inert material called kieselguhr, a silicaceous earth composed of the tiny exoskeletons (shells) of primitive one-celled organisms, diatoms. The mixture consisted of three parts of nitroglycerine to one of kieselguhr. He patented his discovery in 1867 and called it dynamite. He also invented other explosives and from their manufacture and from exploitation of the Baku oil fields (in Azerbaijan, on the Caspian sea), which his elder brother, Robert, managed, Alfred became a very wealthy man.

He filed over 350 patents for his inventions. In 1893 he bought Bofors, a steel works in Varmland, perhaps better known as the arms manufacturer. Disliking pretence and show, he lived a somewhat lonely life, engaged in research. He wrote 'I want to live among trees and bushes, silent friends who respect the state of my nerves and I escape when I can both from large cities and deserts.'

He received many requests for help during his lifetime, but he disliked petitions for memorials. 'I would rather take care of the stomachs of the living rather than the glory of the departed in the form of monuments.' He said 'To spread knowledge is to spread well-being.' No portrait of him was painted until after his death.

Alfred had left Sweden at the age of nine and felt he did not belong anywhere. In 1875 he bought a house in Paris, in the Avenue Malakoff, where he lived on and off for 17 years. In 1890 he bought a villa in San Remo, Italy, 'mio nido' where he died in 1896, alone apart from his servants.

WILL OF ALFRED NOBEL
(translated from the Swedish)

Testament
The whole of my remaining realisable estate shall be dealt with in the following way:

The capital shall be invested by my executors in safe securities and shall constitute a fund, the interest on which shall be distributed in the form of prizes to those who, during the preceding year, shall have conferred the greatest benefit on mankind. The said interest shall be divided into five equal parts, which shall be apportioned as follows:

One part to the person who has made the most important discovery or invention within the field of physics.

One part to the person who shall have made the most important chemical discovery or improvement.
One part to the person who shall have made the most important discovery within the domain of physiology or medicine.

One part to the person who shall have produced in the field of literature the most outstanding work of an idealistic tendency.

One part to the person who shall have done the most or the best work for fraternity among nations, for the abolition or reduction of standing armies and for the holding or promotion of peace congresses.

The prizes for physics and chemistry shall be awarded by the Swedish Academy of Sciences.
That for physiological or medical works by the Carolinska Institute in Stockholm.
That for literature by the Academy in Stockholm.
That for champions of peace by a committee of five persons to be elected by the Norwegian Storting. *

It is my express wish that in awarding the prizes no considera- tion whatever shall be given to the nationality of the candidates; so that the most worthy shall receive the prize, whether he be a Scandinavian or not.

Paris, November 27, 1895.
ALFRED BERNHARD NOBEL

Funeral arrangements had been made by Emanuel Nobel, a nephew of Alfred, and the eldest son of his brother Ludwig, who was manager of the Nobel Brothers Naphtha Company in Baku. A service was held in San Remo, and his body was sent back to Stockholm by train, where formal funeral rites were held in the old Stockholm Cathedral, the Storkyrkan, on 29 December.

Nobel had appointed two executors, a 26-year-old colleague called Ragnar Sohlman who had worked for him as a private assistant, and a 40-year-old industrialist called Rudolph

*Nobel felt that the Norwegian Storting was the most truly democratic organisa- tion to be entrusted with this task. In 1930 a special independent Institute was established to assess candidates for the Peace Prize.

Lilljeqvist. Legal matters were referred to Carl Lindhagen, who was then a Deputy Justice, later to become Lord Mayor of Stockholm.

From the outset there were many problems. 'Magnificent Intentions, magnificent Blunder,' wrote one critic, with the following problems cited:

1. There was doubt as to Nobel's domicile.
2. There were no indications how the prizes were to be awarded, whether the institutions named were in fact willing to undertake these obligations.
3. Nobel's main assets were in France, Russia, Germany and England. Would these countries agree to release them?
4. Where were death duties payable?
5. Which Court had Jurisdiction for probate?
6. The principal legatee, the Nobel Foundation, did not exist.

'You must always remember,' said Emanuel to Ragnar, 'the obligation implied in the Russian word for the executor of a will – *Dushke Prikashshik* – which means "the spokesman for the soul". You must act accordingly.' Sohlman remained very grateful for Emanuel's support and generosity. He stood to lose a great fortune should the will be proved.

However, Nobel's intentions were clear and Sohlman was determined to see them carried out, and he first went to Paris where Nobel had lived for many years, and where he owned a house. The French authorities wanted Nobel to be declared a legal resident, *domicile de fait*, thereby collecting death duties. With the help of the Swedish Consul General in Paris, Gustaf Nordling, who issued a *certificat de coutume*, setting forth Swedish legal practice regarding the rights and privileges of executors of wills, and with the help of the lawyer Lindhagen, who had come to Paris, it was agreed to take possession of Nobel's assets in France.

Using the authority of Nordling's certificates, all the securities were gradually withdrawn from the various banks where they were deposited, and placed in three large *coffres de fort*, at the

Comptoire National d'Escompte. In the meantime Sohlman went to London to engage a lawyer, Timothy Warren, to secure Nobel's English assets.

On his return to Paris, arrangements were made to transfer the securities to London, to the headquarters of the Union Bank of Scotland, and the Enskilda Bank in Stockholm. This was no mean task as huge sums of money were involved. The securities were sent in insured Postal Packages, but the French Post Office refused to cover an excess of 20,000 francs.

The Rothschild banking firm undertook the insurance, on production of the Post Office certificate, provided that no consignment exceeded 2,500,000 francs. Securities to that value were taken daily for a week, to the Expedition de Finances at the Gard du Nord, for transfer to London or Stockholm. Special precautions had to be taken as there was an ever-present risk of hold-ups and robberies. From the bank vaults the papers were packed in a suitcase and taken by horse-drawn cab to the office of the Consulate General, and thence to the Gare du Nord. Sohlman describes how he sat in the cab with a loaded revolver lest there should have been an 'accident'.

This rather odd way of transferring the assets was to prevent the French tax authorities, the dreaded *Fisc*, getting their hands on the money.

While Sohlman was engaged in these activities, two of Nobel's relatives, Hjalmar and Ludwig, had come to discuss with the Consul General the validity of Nobel's will, unaware of Sohlman's presence in another room. With great tact, Nordling delayed informing them of what was happening, but arranged a 'peace and reconciliation' dinner meeting, to be held at the Noel Peter restaurant in the Passage des Princes.

At first the somewhat heavy atmosphere became brighter, but when Sohlman informed Hjalmar and Ludwig that the securities were no longer in France and that the French had no jurisdiction, and that therefore there was no point in them contesting the will in France, but should go to Stockholm, it caused a sensation. At first they refused to believe it, but it was confirmed by Nordling.

Hjalmar then requested a Court Attachment to Nobel's property in France, which was mainly his house in the Avenue Malakoff, thereby preventing its sale.

Assets in Germany (exceeding 6,000,000 kroner) had been secured as Sohlman had previously engaged a lawyer, a Dr Schlarlach, a prominent jurist from Hamburg, who agreed his duties were to protect the interests of the executors.

Hjalmar then went to England in an attempt to get writs of attachment on Nobel's property, but without success.

Back in Sweden, attempts were made to have the will declared invalid, but without success. It was declared that Nobel's domicile, for the purposes of the will, was Bofors, and that the County Court at Karlskoga had jurisdiction. The Paris Court had declared itself incompetent to rule on the question of domicile.

The whole matter was resolved by a decision of the Swedish Government on 21 May 1897, to instruct the Attorney General of Sweden to institute on behalf of the Swedish Government whatever legal actions were necessary to have the will declared valid. And further, the named Institutes were to take measures to ensure that the testator's intentions were carried out.

After protests from certain family members, proceedings began on 30 October 1897, at the County Court at Karlskoga, to report progress on the assets of the estate, which were finally assessed at 31,587,202.28 Kroner net of tax (which amounted to about 10%). This was a lot of money, about $US 9,000,000 – at a time when one could buy a good cigar for 10 cents.

On 1 February 1898, twelve of the twenty relatives who could have benefited from Nobel's estate commenced legal action to contest the will, but withdrew on 5 June 1898, and signed a document declaring they had no further interest in the will and to abstain from any further claims. In return for this, they were to receive the interest on the estate for 1897.

The Swedish Academy of Sciences were also reluctant to accept their obligations under the will, but agreed finally, to accept, with the relatives, provided certain stipulations were added:

1. Nominations were to be approved in consultation with the family of Robert Nobel, and submitted to the approval of the Crown.
2. Each of the Prizes shall be awarded at least once during each 5-year period, shall be not less than 60% of the annual yield of the fund available, and should not be awarded to more than 3 persons.

One day in February 1898, Emanuel Nobel was summoned to the Royal Palace for audience with the king, Oscar II, who pleaded with him to consider the interests of his relatives, and asked him to consider the implications of the Peace Prize, which, he feared, would only lead to controversies and diverse complications. 'Your Uncle has been influenced by peace fanatics, particularly by women,' he declared. Emanuel replied 'Your Majesty perhaps agrees with General Motke – Eternal Peace, that is only a dream, not a beautiful one either.'

He further went on to say that he would not wish his relatives to be reproached in future, by distinguished scientists, for having appropriated funds which properly belong to them.

When he repeated his conversation with the king to his Russian lawyer, the latter took fright and hastily returned to St Petersburg, fearing he might be arrested for *lèse majesté*.

Later the king relented and supported the will, appreciating its high aims, and added to the dignity of the Prize presentations by personally presenting the Prizes on the anniversary of Nobel's death, 10 December.

On 4 July, the Norwegian Storting signified its acceptance of the will, and on 9 September 1898, the Swedish Government gave it its approval.

The Nobel Foundation was set up with a board of five members to take charge of financial management. Prize awarding institutes were established with the right to deduct 25% to cover expenses in connection with selection of examiners, and on 25 September 1900 the trustees of the Nobel Foundation met for the first time, almost four years after Alfred Nobel's death.

Nominations for prizes were to be submitted by Academies of

Science to the Swedish Academy of Science. Initially there were problems because neither USA or UK had an 'Academy of Science', which could submit nominations.

The Prize could not be awarded posthumously, and Rosalind Franklin was deprived of her recognition in connection with her work on the discovery of the structure of DNA, as she had died before the Prize was awarded to Wilkins, Watson and Crick.

Prizes often honour (and sometimes dishonour – Turner Prize) the donor as much as the recipient. They are not without criticism and may be damaging in that they may be unfair and cause intense jealousy, which academics could well do without. Few females have been awarded the Prize. In 1956 Dorothy Hodgson, described as a housewife and mother of three, had determined the chemical structure of Vitamin B_{12}, cyanocobalamine, the remedy in tiny doses (an injection of 1mg per month) of pernicious anaemia and the neurological condition subacute combined degeneration of the spinal cord. The Prize for Chemistry was awarded to her Head of Department and to a Russian chemist. In 1964 she was eventually awarded the Prize, only the fifth woman so to be honoured.

The first prizes were awarded on 10 December 1901, five years after Nobel's death. One was awarded to Wilhelm Röntgen for his discovery of X-rays.

The Nobel committee has had a difficult task in interpreting Nobel's wishes, that the discovery should be for the benefit of mankind. In 1909 they had no problem, the Physics Prize was awarded to Marconi for his demonstration of the ability of radio waves to cross the Atlantic Ocean, which he achieved in 1901. They had to distinguish between Pure and Applied Science, and generally went for pure Science.

The existence of the Prize has introduced a spirit of competition into Science, which may not always be helpful.

The Prize for Literature has always been a difficult one as Nobel's Will directed that it should be of an idealistic nature. It might be thought that Ibsen and Tolstoy would be good candidates, but they failed to be awarded the Prize as they were considered too radical and critical of existing institutions, political and religious. Kipling, however, got one. As is often the way with Prizes, they often tell us more about the donor than the recipient.

The Peace Prize is another controversial one. The first one was awarded to Bertha von Suttner, a friend of Nobel's, who campaigned for Peace Congresses. In 1906 it was awarded to Theodore Roosevelt for his part in bringing to an end the Russo-Japanese war, a decision that caused much controversy.

During the First World War (1914–1918) few Prizes were awarded and the income was donated to relief work.

The Prize for Literature was awarded to George Bernard Shaw in 1925. He commented in his acceptance speech that not only was dynamite a particularly diabolical invention but that it required a particularly diabolical mind to think of a Prize for Literature.

There is no doubt that the award of the Peace Prize has political overtones. The Peace Prize for 1935 was awarded to the pacifist writer Carl von Ossietski who campaigned against Hitler, revealing details of the rearmament of Germany, which was common knowledge, and who was imprisoned by Hitler for treason.

Goering had tried to persuade Ossietski to refuse the Prize, but he eventually accepted it, though the money was later embezzled by a Berlin lawyer to whom Ossietski had given power of attorney. Ossietski died in prison in 1938, of tuberculosis.

After that Hitler issued a decree that no German was permitted to accept the Prize. Hitler and Mussolini had been nominated for Peace Prizes by the fascist organisation Fedrelandslaget (League of Patriots).

The value of the award depends on the income from the Trust. In 1928 it was US$42,060. In 1922, when Albert Einstein received the Prize for his work in connection with photo-electricity, it was worth US$20,000.

The Prize is not always awarded. It has come to be the highest scientific accolade, and there is intense competition. In 1968 a sixth Prize - the Nobel Memorial Prize in Economics was set up by the Central Bank of Sweden, to be administered by the

Central Bank and the Nobel Foundation. It was not strictly a Nobel Prize since it was not mentioned in Nobel's will. In 1994 it was awarded to the American recovered schizophrenic mathematician John Nash, together with Reinhard Selten and John Harsanyi, for their work on 'rationality and equilibrium in Strategic interaction' better known as 'Game Theory'. This was used as the basis for the auction of radiofrequency channels to be allotted to the various mobile user companies. From December 1994 until March 1995 Vice-President Al Gore supervised the auction which netted the US Government $7 billion, the biggest sale of public assets in American history. A similar strategy in the UK netted the Government £22.47 billion for third generation (2.4Ghz) mobile channels. In France it was £12bn, in Italy £7bn, in Sweden £10,000. Perhaps 3G should stand for Girls, Gambling and Games, with the latter predominating.

In 1991 the Prize was worth 6 million Kroner, equivalent to £400,000. In 1992 the Prize for Literature was awarded to the West Indian poet Derek Walcott for his epic poem *Omeros*, a vast narrative based on the *Iliad* and *Odyssey* of the Greek poet Homer, consisting of 2,500 stanzas of rhyming hexameters. It was worth £690,000 ($US1,200,000).

In 1993, the Prize for Literature was awarded to the 62-year-old black American writer Toni Morrison (formerly Chloe Antony Wofford) for her novels, characterised by visionary force and poetic impact. It was worth £563,000.

The Nobel committee does not always get it right. In 1903 the committee awarded the Prize to Neils Finsen a Danish physician for a treatment for a skin condition that proved unimportant. In 1908 a French physicist received the Prize for a system of colour photography that came to nothing. In 1926 Johannes Fibiger, a Danish physician, received the Prize for a theory that certain cancers were caused by a parasitic worm. It later emerged that the worm had no relation to the disease.

One of the most glaring omissions was the failure of the Nobel committee to include the name of the American physiologist Charles Best in the award of the Prize to Frederick Banting and John Macleod in 1923 for the discovery of insulin.

In 1992 the Peace Prize was awarded to Rigoberta Menchu who had written a book, *I Rigoberta Menchu*, purporting to be an autobiography describing a massacre at her home town Chajul, Guatamala. It subsequently transpired that the account was put together by Elizabeth Burgos, former wife of a communist writer Regis Debray, and that the Nobel committee had been deceived. She was chosen because she was what they wanted – a Mayan woman victim of a cruel regime, symbolising the plight of the dispossessed Indians. Perhaps the warnings of Oscar II should have been heeded.

But the most misguided Prize was awarded in 1949 to the Portuguese psychiatrist Antonio Egas Moniz for the introduction of lobotomy (leucotomy) as a treatment for mental disorder. This is the metaphorical equivalent of ramming a screwdriver into the central processing unit of a malfunctioning computer in the vain hope that in some unspecified way it might restore normal function.

Unfortunately, and ironically, he was unable to attend the presentation ceremony as he was in a wheelchair. He was para-plegic, having been shot in the back by one of his former patients. Psychiatry is a hazardous specialty, very stressful, with an above average suicide rate, and, in the NHS, an opportunity for early retirement at the age of 55.

SCIENCE FRAUD, ALLEGED FRAUD, AND ERROR

False facts are highly injurious to the progress of science, for they often endure long; but false views, if supported by some evidence, do little harm, for everyone takes salutary pleasure proving their falseness.

Darwin.

The belief in a claimed phenomenon causes one to see in marginal data evidence when there is none, to explain away contrary evidence, and to believe in effects which are not reproducible and are seen, if at all, at the limits of experimental error.

Frank Close

Perhaps fraud should be defined as the exploitation of the gullible by the unscrupulous. At any rate, it is the deliberate deception, by an individual or a group, for the purposes of gain, whether social or financial.

1. PHLOGISTON THEORY

No account of the history of science would be complete without mentioning the Phlogiston Theory. Though not strictly fraud, it is an example of misinterpretation, an erroneous attempt to explain certain phenomena, and serves as an object lesson and a salutary warning.

The idea originated with a German chemist, J.J. Becher, about 1700, and was taken up by G.E. Stahl, one time physician to the King of Prussia. It was necessary to explain what happened when a substance burnt. The theory proposed that a combustible substance consisted of two parts, a calx (Latin: ash) and phlogiston (Greek: anything set on fire). In the process of burning, phlogiston escaped and the calx remained. It explained the fact that flames can transfer heat. The observation that a metal, such as magnesium actually increased in weight when it burnt was ignored, or explained by assuming that phlogiston had a negative weight. The nature of gases was completely unknown at the time and it was not until the French scientist Lavoisier about 1780, based on the observations of the English scientist Priestley (who actually believed in phlogiston), correctly explained the phenomenon of burning and named the gas involved, previously called de-phlogisticated air, oxygen. 'Inflammable air' he called – hydrogen – water producer. The English scientist Henry Cavendish had established the composition of water, and the residual gas of air he called 'azote' – without life, later to be called nitrogen.

2. CALORIC

This was erroneously thought to be a subtle fluid that was transferred from one object or fluid to another when they were heated, or came into contact with each other. Many eminent scientists including Lavoisier believed in Caloric, but by the early nineteenth century the ideas of Benjamin Thompson, Count Rumford, prevailed and it became clear that heat was a form of energy due to motion of the molecules – thermal agitation.

3. PILTDOWN MAN – BONES STONES AND EGOS

In June 1912, Charles Dawson, then aged 48, a practising solicitor in Uckfield Sussex, and an amateur geologist and archaeologist, and Arthur Woodward, also 48, and a vertebrate paleontologist and Keeper of Geology at the British Museum, were exploring a gravel pit at Barkham Manor (Piltdown) in Sussex when they came across some fossil fragments. They appeared to have come from a human skull. There were three pieces of parietal bone and one piece of occipital bone. In addition, there were pieces of teeth of a primitive elephant, and teeth of a beaver and horse, together with various flints (eoliths) which appear to be dated in the late Pleistocene period (170,000 years ago), or early Pleiocene period. On 30 August a canine tooth was found by Pierre Teilhard de Chardin, a Jesuit Priest who was taking a spiritual retreat at Ore Place, Hastings, and was spending a few days with Dawson before returning to France.

As background to the significance of these events it is instructive to remember that the 1611 Bible authorised by King James I of England dated the creation to be 4004BC. In the eighteenth century geological studies suggested the age of the Earth to be several hundred million years (the Bible is not intended to teach science or history: it is to guide men in faith and conduct). The controversy over the origin of Man was further aggravated by the publication of *Origin of Species* by Charles Darwin in 1859.

On 18 December 1912, Dawson presented his nine cranial fragments, to form a skull 150mm wide and 190mm long, to the Geological Society. The question was, was this the Missing Link between anthropoid apes and man? (The jaw appeared more ape-like).

Gravel at Galley Hill in Kent, where a possibly paleolithic skull had been found in 1888 at the 100 foot terrace was geologically dated to the last of the temperate intervals before the Ice Age, 100,000 years ago, though Piltdown was at the 130 foot level, suggesting even greater antiquity. Dr Arthur Keith, an anatomist and Conservator of the Hunterian Museum of the Royal College of Surgeons of England, although maintaining the authenticity of the fragments, disagreed with their reconstruction and an acrimonious correspondence followed between Keith and Woodward. Further fragments were found in 1915 at Sheffield Park, a few miles from Barkham Manor (Piltdown 2). Unfortunately Dawson fell ill and died on 10 August 1916.

The Great War curtailed further study, but fragments of early Man were found as follows:

1921 – 2 Human Molar teeth were found 30 miles SW of Peking.

1924 – Humanoid skull of uncertain date was found at Taung, 80 miles North of Kimberley, S. Africa.

1932 – Louis Leakey found fragments of a human jaw at Kanam and cranial fragments at Kanjura, Kenya, E. Africa.

1935 – A Clapham dentist Alvan Marston found fragments of

a middle Pleistocene Man at Swanscombe in Kent and stimulated further investigations into Piltdown Man.

In the late nineteenth century a French mineralogist Adolphe Carnot devised a method of dating by fluorine content. With the passage of time concentration of fluorine in bone increases. This test was used by Dr Kenneth Oakley, a geologist and palaeontologist of the British Museum of Natural History. In 1948 he confirmed the antiquity of the Swanscombe fragments by measuring their fluorine content at 2% (experimental error plus or minus 0.2%). The Piltdown fragments only gave 0.4 to 0.1%.

In 1953 Joseph Wiener, a South African anthropologist working with W.E. Le Gros Clarke, anatomist and Reader in Physical Anthropology at Oxford University, became convinced that the Piltdown fragments were forgeries. Drilling the canine tooth showed that, under the stained surface, the dentine was white, probably coming from an ape, consistent with recent origin. Also the tooth had the fine marks characteristic of filing. Further analysis showed that the nitrogen content, which indicates loss of organic material, was too high for the alleged antiquity. More accurate dating using uranium radioactivity suggested the tooth had if fact come from Tunis. The jaw bone was almost certainly from a hominid ape, probably an Urang-Otan. The cranial fragments and flints had been stained to match the gravels. Soil analysis showed the chemical conditions to be at variance with the fossil remains, which had almost certainly been imported.

But who did it? Who had method opportunity and motive? Wiener pursued the matter. A local retired biology teacher, Robert Essex, was convinced that Teilhard de Chardin was responsible, presumably to discredit English anthropologists. Dawson had been observed staining bones, presumably he sought fame and to be elected FRS. Others wished to further their careers.

Perhaps we will never know. There must have been a certain amount of patriotic fervour. After all, the Germans had Neanderthal Man (discovered in 1857 in the valley of the Dussel, a tributary of the Rhine.) The French had the caves and drawings at Les Eyzies, near Sarlat in the Dordogne, the Spanish Altamira, in Cantabria, near Santander in 1879. ('Toros, Toros!' exclaimed the five-year-old daughter of the Marquis de Sautuola, holding up a candle to the ceiling of the cave, into which she had wandered while her father was looking for bone implements, the first human eyes to view them for over ten thousand years. They were not bulls but aurochs (the tribal totem), a relative of the bison, ancestor of present-day cattle, a species that became extinct in the seventeenth century, the last one dying in Poland. It is possible that there are descendants at Chillingham, Northumberland).

4. Sir Cyril Burt: The Case of the Missing Twins.

Cyril Burt was born on 3 March 1883, the eldest son of a country practitioner. A neighbour of his was Sir Francis Galton, anthropologist and geneticist and a cousin of Charles Darwin. Cyril was a bright and intelligent child, sensitive and not physically robust, who managed to obtain scholarships to Christ's Hospital School and Jesus College Oxford, where he read Classical Greats. This was a four-year course where five terms were spent learning Greek and Latin languages and literature (Moderations), and seven terms learning ancient history, logic, ethics and philosophy (Literae Humanitories). It does not fit one for any specific vocation but tends to induce an attitude of effortless superiority, and thus eminently suited to the higher ranks of the Civil Service.

A readership in Mental Philosophy had been set up and Burt studied psychology under William Mc Dougall. He obtained second class honours in his final examinations. He then spent a year obtaining a teachers' diploma at Clifton College, after which he obtained a scholarship to the University of Wurzburg.

The world's first psychology laboratory had been set up in 1879 by Wundt, in Leipzig. So in the summer of 1908 Burt arrived in Wurzburg, but later in the year returned to England to take up a post as assistant lecturer in physiology and experimental psychology at the University of Liverpool, for three years, at a salary of £150 per year. In fact he stayed for five years, and met and was influenced by the famous physiologist Sir

Charles Sherrington who had written *The Integrative action of the Nervous System*.

Burt developed and carried out intelligence tests in children which appeared to confirm his belief in the genetic basis of intelligence. In 1913 the Mental Deficiency Act was passed and Burt was appointed Psychologist to the London County Council, at the age of 30. This Act required children to be classified as Idiots, Imbeciles, Feeble Minded, or Morally Defective, and Burt was asked to do this assessment.

In 1914 the war broke out but Burt was rejected for military service on the grounds of flat feet, short sightedness and 'disorderly action of the heart' – a condition no longer recognised.

As a consequence of his work, in 1921 he published *Mental and Scholastic Tests* which became a standard manual for educational psychologists for the next 30 years and was reprinted many times. In 1925 he published *The Young Delinquent*, and in 1937 *The Backward Child*.

From 1924 until 1932 he was appointed Professor of Educational Psychology at the London Day Training College, later to become the Institute of Education of London University, and in 1932 married Joyce Woods. He was then 49 and she was 23. They had no children, probably at Burts' request.

In 1932 he was appointed Professor of Psychology at University College at a salary of £1,000 a year, where he remained until 1939. At the outbreak of war his department was transferred to Aberystwyth in Wales. His wife did not accompany him, in fact she had been studying medicine and had become a gynaecologist.

On 16 April 1941, at the height of the blitz (Second World War) a bomb fell on his house in Gower Street, London. All his records, his life's work, were destroyed. It was probably the shock and distress of this that led to his subsequent behaviour. Later that year Burt developed Menieres's disease, characterised by giddiness, tinnitus and deafness, and this was to plague him for the rest of his life, and may well have been responsible for his subsequent actions.

In 1943 he published *Ability and Income* and referred to his twin studies. He reported on 156 pairs of non-identical twins,

62 pairs of identical twins, of whom 15 had been reared apart. The correlation of IQs of non-identical twins was 0.54, of unseparated identical twins 0.86, and of separated twins 0.77.

In 1946 he was knighted for his work for education and the armed services, the first psychologist to be so honoured.

In 1950 he retired from his position as professor, with great reluctance, and by then he had become increasingly devious in his relationships. He would write letters to his journal *The Statistical Journal of the British Psychological Society*, of which he was editor, under pseudonyms.

In 1955 he wrote in an article 'The concept of intelligence', 'Thanks to my assistant Miss Conway the number of twins has increased,' stating that a further 172 pairs of non-identical twins have been identified, 83 identical twins reared together and 21 reared apart, and that by virtue of various tests he had concluded that intelligence was 87% genetic and 13% environmental.

In 1966 a further 32 identical twins reared apart (a very rare occurrence) had somehow been identified.

Other researchers who contacted Burt with requests for original data were fobbed off with excuses that they had been lost or destroyed, which was true, but Burt had 'creatively remembered' (or rather fabricated) them. He was becoming increasingly difficult and mildly paranoid. His views had helped establish the 11+ examination and selective education, but by 1965 these were abandoned and comprehensive schools were set up, no doubt to his distress.

Burt died in October 1971, of liver cancer, at the age of 88. On 16 October 1972 the medical correspondent of *The Times*, Oliver Gillie, inserted an advertisement requesting Margaret Howard or J. Conway or anyone who had assisted Sir Cyril Burt in his studies of the intelligence of twins to come forward and please contact him. Eight days later, after a negative response, he wrote an article exposing Burt's fraud in graphic terms. 'Crucial data was faked by eminent psychologist' – 'Theories of IQ pioneer completely discredited'.

The truth of the matter was difficult to ascertain, as Burt's earlier research papers had been destroyed. But it appears that no original research was done after 1950, and probably none after

1940. Burt kept a comprehensive dairy of his day-to-day activities and there was no mention of meetings with Miss Conway or Miss Howard. The identity of these ladies was uncertain. They may have been LCC social workers, but they were not on any salaried payroll. More likely they were voluntary Care Committee workers, who had assisted Burt in his earlier researches. Both these ladies contributed letters and articles to Burt's *Statistical Journal*, but they were almost certainly written by Burt and ceased when he stopped being editor.

He may well have been right that nature counts for more than nurture (?85%:15%) in final achievement. He believed that progressive education had led to declining standards, most marked in English composition, where bad grammar, bad spelling, and the crudest vulgarisms were no longer frowned upon.

Unfortunately his fabrication of evidence led to his work falling into disrepute. The matter remains unresolved.

5.   COLD FUSION: THE CASE OF THE MISSING NEUTRONS

On 23 March 1989, two chemists, working in the University of Utah, Martin Fleischman and Stanley Pons, called a press conference. The subject was cold fusion. They claimed to have produced energy by the same process that the Sun derives its energy, by nuclear reactions, but at room temperature. They were electrochemists, and claimed to have produced excess heat (four watts out for one watt in) in a simple electrolytic cell using palladium electrodes and an electrolyte of lithium deuteroxide.

The idea was that deuterium atoms (^2H – heavy hydrogen, whose nucleus contains one proton and one neutron) when 'charged' into palladium (which was known to have a high affinity for hydrogen – 500 times its volume) would 'fuse' and liberate vast quantities of energy. If fusion was occurring, excess heat, neutrons and gamma radiation would be produced. In addition, helium (^3He) and the highly radioactive tritium (^3H) should be formed. Considerations of National Security arose as tritium, with a half-life of 18.5 years, is the basis of the H-bomb, and if it could be manufactured easily and cheaply the results could be catastrophic (Indian scientists were particularly interested in this one). Early on in their experiments, a block of palladium had mysteriously vaporised and been destroyed, which led them to believe they were on the right track.

Unfortunately, Fleischman and Pons had little experience of nuclear physics and did not have the necessary apparatus to measure the neutrons or radiation. At nearby Brigham Young University, Steven Jones and Paul Palmer were working on an allied subject of muon catalysed fusion and did have neutron measuring equipment. Fleischman and Pons took their 'cell' to Jones and believed, incorrectly, that they had seen excess neutrons (the detection of neutrons requires very sophisticated apparatus, weighing over a ton, in order to screen it from stray background neutrons). In addition, if deuteron fusion was occurring, characteristic gamma rays emitted should have been at an energy of 2.224 million electron volts. Radiation at 2.5 MEV was identified and somehow was incorrectly measured. Subsequently Fleischman and Pons were reluctant to admit this error.

On March 6th 1989, President Petersen of the University of Utah and President Holland of Brigham Young University held a 'summit' conference ('There are billions of dollars at stake here and Nobels in the offing'), to decide how the research was to be released. Both sets of scientists said they would like more time to confirm their results. However they were pressed and agreed to a joint submission on 24 March, and to send their papers to *Nature*. The universities' main concern was to patent the process, thus earning millions of dollars in royalties.

In the meantime Fleischmann had tried to get his cell to Harwell in England for analysis of the neutron spectrum but the Customs and Excise Department had refused its transport on the grounds that it might be radioactive. Later, he informed Harwell how to set it up, and on 21 Martin Fleischmann received a fax saying they had seen nothing. He tried, unsuccessfully, to get the press conference cancelled, and booked a flight home to England on 24 March.

On 7 April the Governor of Utah, Norman Bangeter convened an emergency session of the State Legislature and an appropriation of $5 million was voted 96 to 3 for fusion research. *Nature* had declined to publish the papers. Said the Governor 'We are not going to allow some English magazine decide how State money is handled.'

There were two major criticisms of the work. Firstly, that no control experiment had been done using ordinary water instead of heavy water. And secondly, that the gamma ray emission was at the wrong energy level.

The fact was that even on theoretical grounds fusion of deuterium nuclei was unlikely. X-ray crystallography had shown that they are 0.17 nanometers apart in palladium, and their bond distance was 0.07 nanometers (though it must be said here that progress in science occurs when experiment contradicts theory).

One of the problems was that the scientists wanted to tell everything, but the patent attorneys 'tell us to say absolutely nothing'. The relevant cells were under lock and key at the University of Utah, and no information had been published, so all scientists trying to repeat the experiments were working in the dark. Scientists trying to contact the university found the phone lines perpetually blocked by journalists and cranks. Everyone desperately wanted to believe in it yet the evidence against it was mounting. The trouble was that negative results do not make headlines, do not get published.

One scientist, observing the experiment on television, commented – 'the man explaining the experiment to reporters was apparently touching the glass bulb containing the active elements yet none of his bodily parts fell off'. If fusion had in fact been occurring, intense radiation would have been produced. It was even being claimed that the big oil companies, fearing loss of income, had bought them off and suppressed the information.

On 1 May at a meeting of the American Physical Society, Nathan Lewis, an electrochemist from Caltech, said 'we looked at this, we looked at that, we saw nothing.'

On 15 June the Atomic Energy Research Laboratory at Harwell announced that they were ceasing research into cold fusion. 'Results to date have been disappointing and we can no longer justify devoting further resources to this area.'

It has been estimated that $40 million had been spent in

investigating the claim. Six weeks' work, four nuclear physicists six electrochemists and over a hundred experiments searching for neutrons, radiation, tritium or helium, all with negative results. Even so, Utah was reluctant to concede defeat. Said James Brophy, University vice-president for research, 'It is disappointing that they have not been able to do the experiments properly.'

The saga dragged on, at least in the USA. The National Institute for Cold Fusion, funded by the University of Utah, was increasingly called into question, and its protagonist, Chase Petersen, resigned as University President in July 1991.

Perhaps the moral of the story is that those responsible for disbursing large sums of money should know something of scientific method. Unfortunately, they are more likely to be arts graduates than science graduates.

6. The Baltimore Case: The Case of the Missing Clones
(A Cautionary Tale, but with a happy ending).

On April 25th, 1986, a paper was published in the journal *Cell* on the rather arcane subject of antibody production in transgenic mice: 'Altered Repertoire of Endogenous Immunoglobulin Gene Expression in Transgenic Mice Containing a Rearranged Mu Heavy Chain Gene'. In it, it was claimed that antibodies to foreign protein were produced in transgenic mice in addition to native ones. The authors were D. Weaver, Moema H. Reis, Christopher Albanese, Frank Constantini, David Baltimore, and Thereza Imanishi-Kari.

David Baltimore, had won the Nobel Prize in 1975 for his discovery, in conjunction with Howard Tumin, of the enzyme reverse transcriptase which catalyses the transformation of virus RNA to DNA, which then incorporates in a host cell genome and replicates, destroying it – T4 helper cells in the case of HIV, the cause of AIDS. In 1982 he asked David Weaver, a molecular biochemist, to establish if transgenic mice could produce transgenic antibodies. Weaver then asked Theresa Imanishi-Kari for help in the immunological antibody studies. This involved injecting cells into a vein in a mouse's tail, using a very fine needle, a difficult technical procedure. She asked Margot O'Toole, a post doctorate fellow, for help. Unfortunately, these two did not get on.

IK, who was of Japanese birth, was seven years older than O'T. Her parents had emigrated to Brazil. Her sister had died of 'Lupus' – Systemic Lupus Erythematosis, an immunological disease in which the body makes antibodies to its own white cells. IK was fluent in seven languages, but her English was sometimes difficult to understand.

O'T was of Irish birth, interested in politics. In 1985 IK and O'T, disagreed over certain cell transfer experiments, O'T accusing IK of faking results. Sometimes O'T could not get the experiments to work. O'T approached Charles Mablethorpe, who had also fallen out with IK, and was not happy in the laboratory, for help.

O'T suggested the paper should be withdrawn. This was refused and she approached the Ombudswoman of Massachusetts Institute of Technology, Mary Rowe, who discussed the matter with Baltimore. He suggested the matter could best be resolved by further experiment, not by arguing about it. DB suggested that O'T write a letter to *Cell*. This she declined, and was annoyed because no correction was to be published.

Mablethorpe approached Ned Feder and Walter W. Stewart, a pair of fraud busters, for help, and Stewart contacted O'T, who gave him seventeen pages of IK's notes she had copied, to try to establish fraud. Mary Miers of the National Institute of Health decided to establish a group to consider the evidence. In the winter of 1988, Feder and Stewart went to Capitol Hill to discuss scientific fraud with Bruce Chafin and Peter Stockton, who worked for Representative John Dingell, Chairman of the House Energy and Commerce Committee, which had jurisdiction over the NIH. Dingell was of course interested in ensuring correct use of Government, i.e. taxpayer, funds ($6billion per annum budget). These three went about their business in a somewhat aggressive manner, assuming guilt until proved otherwise, and had a soft spot for whistleblowers.

They considered all O'Ts evidence, none of IK's, and castigated NIH for inadequate investigation. The *New England Journal of*

Medicine commented – 'They have set themselves up as Grand Inquisitors... the dispute had no business in being aired in public.' The Secret Service was called in to analyse some data, alleging that dates had been altered, notes had been overwritten, certain experiments involving cloning had not in fact been performed.

In March 1989, the Office of Scientific Integrity was created to investigate misconduct. In April 1990, IK's research grant was suspended. No explanation was given. IK's lawyer advised her not to communicate with the OSI until the charges were formulated and the evidence produced. She had given the OSI her notebooks but was not allowed to see them. A draft report showed IK to be guilty of scientific fraud. This was leaked to John Dingell's committee and a storm of antagonism arose. David Baltimore resigned as President of Rockefeller University.

In April 1993 there was independent confirmation of the findings of the original *Cell* paper.

In April 1994 IK received the final report, eight years after the original allegations had been made and she immediately appealed. 'For the first time in all these years I could see the so-called evidence.'

In June 1995 the appeals committee met and allowed the appeal, preferring IK's evidence to that of O'T, but principally on the grounds that due process (correct procedure – the Five Pillars of Justice) had not been followed. That is to say:

1. The accused has the right be informed of the charges.
2. The accused has the right to see the evidence.
3. The accused or advocate has the right to present and examine witnesses.
4. The accused or advocate has the right to cross examine witnesses.
5. The accused has the right to be heard before a panel of neutral judges.

Not only must justice be done, it must be seen to be done. Therefore hearings should be in open court.

The allegation that the cloning experiment had not been performed was found to be irrelevant to the conclusions of the paper. The Secret Service evidence was found to be seriously flawed. The nineteen counts of fraud and misconduct constituted an indictment rather than a verdict.

On June 1996 IK was exonerated on all nineteen charges and was reinstated as assistant professor at Tufts University in June 1997, with tenure. The *New York Times* wrote that the outcome vindicated the long and eventually lonely campaign that Baltimore had waged in her defence.

In May 1997 David Baltimore was named President of the California Institute of Technology.

7. THE CASE OF THE MIDWIFE TOAD

On 23 September 1926, the body of the 45-year-old respected experimental biologist Dr Paul Kammerer was found on a mountain path on the Schneeberg in Austria, by the Theresa rock. In his right hand was a revolver. His suicide note contained the sardonic phrase 'perhaps my worthy academic colleagues will discover in my brain a trace of the qualities they found absent from the manifestation of my mental activities while I was alive'. A tragic end to a brilliant career.

Kammerer's obituary notice in *Nature* called his last book 'one of the finest contributions to the theory of evolution which has appeared since Darwin.

He was accused of fraud, of which he was almost certainly innocent, and the rejection of his work by his scientific colleagues was the last straw. It is a strange story. Kamnmerer had an extraordinary affinity for reptiles and amphibians. He was able to breed them in captivity. He succeeded when all others had failed, and no doubt there was a considerable element of jealousy amongst his academic colleagues. He was a wizard with lizards.

He named his daughter Lacerta after a species of lizard. Once, at a party in Moravia, he picked up a rare variety of toad and kissed it tenderly on the head. The old chatelaine, observing this, almost swooned and called him '*Krotenkusser*' (toad kisser).

He thought that, under certain circumstances (adaptation to current environment), acquired characteristics could be inherited. This was Lamarck's theory, and was considered heresy by respectable Darwinians, largely because the mechanism by which this was achieved could not be explained. Kammerer managed to get specimens of the Midwife Toad (*Alytes obstetricans*) to breed in captivity.

Most toads live and breed in water, but the Midwife Toad was adapted to life in a dry environment, and the fertilised eggs, instead of lying in water, remain stuck to the hind legs of the male. During the mating season, the normal male toad develops black, horny spined swellings on his hands so that he can grasp the female round the waist. These are called 'nuptial pads'. The Midwife Toad, mating on dry land, does not need these, and does not develop them. Kammerer managed to get *Alytes* to mate in water and was able to demonstrate, after many years and generations, the appearance of these nuptial pads, which were inherited by their offspring. This was in 1909.

He also experimented with the primitive Ascidian sea-squirt *Ciona intestinalis,* that cutting off its tubes induced them to grow longer, a character which was then inherited.

In addition, he was able to get the lizard Salamandra to alter its skin colour by providing a different background, and that this also was inherited.

One of his best known experiments was to restore sight to the blind cave-dwelling newt Proteus by exposing it to red light during development, again inheritable.

There ware many doubters. One of these was Professor William Bateson, of Cambridge University, who was of course a firm believer in Darwinian orthodoxy.

Kammerer's great misfortune was that his laboratory and all his experimental animals perished in the Great War of 1914–1918, except for one rather shrivelled specimen of *Alytes*. This was examined in Vienna in 1926 by Dr G.K. Noble, Curator of Reptiles of the American Museum of Natural History, who found that it had been injected with Indian ink so as to demonstrate the black nuptial pads, and was a fake. His report was published six weeks before Kammerer shot himself.

Just who did that fatal injection was never established. It could have been an over-enthusiastic laboratory assistant. It was

almost certainly not Kammerer. Just because one cannot con-
ceive a molecular mechanism for the inheritance of acquired
characteristics is not a valid reason for rejecting outright the
possibility. In fact recent work with micro-organisms seems to
confirm that the possibility does exist. The basis of this is that
the genetic code is not a static structure but in a state of change,
like everything else, and a variety of stimuli can affect that
structure.

8. The Case of the Missing Nurses

In 1977, in Geelong, Victoria, Michael Briggs was appointed
Foundation Dean of Science and Professor of Human Biology to
the newly fledged Deakin University. His CV was said to be
twenty pages long, and his specialty was oral contraceptives,
their biology and safety profile. He was a powerful character,
had a high opinion of himself and an ability to attract grant
money from drug companies.

In 1980 he wrote letters to doctors in the USA advising them
to prescribe an oral contraceptive produced by his largest donor,
on the basis of research findings that appeared to have been
fabricated, and data from tests involving nurses from Geelong
Hospital that had almost certainly not been done.

In late 1983, Dr Rossiter, a paediatrician on the University
council and chairmen of the ethics committee, approached the
University Chancellor, Judge Austin Asche, with this evidence,
suggesting that there should be an independent inquiry. Asche
disagreed, and told Rossiter to write to Briggs. This he did, and
received an unsatisfactory reply. This convinced the Vice-
Chancellor, Professor Fred Jevons, that an inquiry was merited.
However Briggs approached the University Visitor, a curious and
archaic institution who had powers to arbitrate in disputes, and
the inquiry was quashed.

In 1985, a second inquiry began, but by this time Briggs had
retired and settled in the Costa del Sol in Spain. He was interviewed by reporters from the *Sunday Times* and defended his reputation. Two months later he was dead, at the age of 51, reput-
edly of liver failure.

The reputation of Deakin University suffered as a consequence of this affair, which gave rise to much local animosity, pro- and anti-Briggs.

9. THE CASE OF THE MISSING RABBITS

In 1982, a research scientist, Phil Vardy, working at Foundation 41, an institute devoted to the study of birth defects at Sydney Australia, and founded by Dr William McBride, opened a letter containing a reprint of an article in the *Australian Journal of Biological Science*. This purported to be by McBride, Vardy and French (another research worker at the Institute), reporting the teratogenicity of the drug hyoscine. It alleged that hyoscine had been given to pregnant rabbits with adverse effects. Vardy went back to the original work which had been done a few months earlier and found many discrepancies. There were no controls, the numbers were not significant. The rabbit foetuses, said to have been sectioned and examined microscopically, were still in their pots.

Dr McBride's claim to fame went back to 1961, when he had written a letter to *The Lancet* drawing attention to birth defects, possibly due to the drug Thalidomide alpha-phthalyl glutarimide. It was called Contergan in Germany where it was developed, and Distaval in the UK. It was never licensed for use in USA. It was marketed as a sedative but unfortunately it was found that pregnant women who were taking it on the 33rd day of gestation gave birth to babies otherwise normal but with reduced or absent arms and legs – the greatest disaster in the history of Materia Medica.

In the late 1970s Dr McBride was alleging that the drug Debendox (also known as Bendictine) was teratogenic. He was appearing for the plaintiffs, claiming damages in litigation, in the USA. He never won but the manufacturers were forced to withdraw the drug as the legal costs of further defence were prohibitive. Presumably he was using the bogus rabbit experiments in order to provide evidence to support his claim.

Vardy was unaware of all this at the time but confronted McBride with 'his problem'. He got nowhere. He approached the Dean of the Medical Faculty of the University of New South Wales (who was also on Foundation 41's research advisory committee) and was told to 'keep his head down as he could not win in this situation'. But seven other scientists working in Foundation 41 supported him and wrote to the committee insisting on an inquiry. This took place some months later after Vardy had resigned, and found that McBride could not justify the changes to the paper and insisted that it be retracted. This was never done. The researchers who supported Vardy and French were told that there was insufficient funding for their posts and to reapply for them. They took the Foundation to the Industrial Court but received no satisfaction. Six of the seven left.

In December 1987 a radio broadcast was made by Norman Swan, who had met Vardy by accident. Dr McBride refused to be interviewed, but there was widespread media interest, and Dr McBride fought back protesting his innocence. The board of Foundation 41 supported him for 6 months but eventually relented and set up an inquiry under Sir Harry Gibbs, former Chief Justice of Australia. They found that Dr McBride had indeed committed scientific fraud, and he resigned, only to be reinstated as a director after a coup in which the Foundation's board were replaced.

He then had to face disciplinary proceedings before the Medical Tribunal of New South Wales. Fifteen complaints were brought against him, nine relating to clinical practice, six to allegations of scientific misconduct. This hearing became the longest against a doctor in history, costing the taxpayer millions of dollars, and in July 1993 his name was struck off the Register of Doctors of New South Wales. He was then aged 67 and was in the USA.

10. The Case of the Missing Mother and Baby

In August 1994, a paper appeared in *The British Journal of Obstetrics and Gynaecology* entitled 'Term delivery after intrauterine relocation of an ectopic pregnancy'.

The authors were J.M. Pearce, I.T. Manyonda, and G.V.P. Chamberlain of St George's Hospital, London. They claimed to have transplanted an ectopic pregnancy into the uterus, successfully, with a live baby, a procedure that had never before been achieved. Unfortunately, neither the baby nor its mother could be found, and there was evidence that computer records had been tampered with and Mr Pearce was swiftly suspended.

This case had wider implications concerning the nature of 'gift authorship'. Neither Manyonda nor Professor Chamberlain had much to do with the work or the writing of the paper. Prof. Chamberlain, who at the time was Pearce's head of department and an editor of the journal, twice asked for his name to be removed. It was not and he resigned. It only took nine months for the hearing to take place. The reason for this speed was that the Principal of the Medical School, Sir William Asscher, 'knew what to do and was determined to do it.'

The 'BMJ' commented – 'Research papers are so seldom checked that scores of bogus papers are probably published annually, securing fame, promotion and future funding for the author in the form of research grants. Particularly in a society which measures worth by the weight of papers produced rather than their quality. Too often the affair would have been brushed under the carpet and the whistle blower probably hounded out of office.' Gift authors were strongly advised to take responsibility for the papers to which they attached their names.

11. The Case of the Missing Professor

In the 1980s Professor V.J. Gupta of the University of Chandrigar described fossils allegedly obtained by himself from various difficult and inaccessible areas, with the object of determining the ages of rocks of the Himalayas.

The Professor would send samples of fossil materials to other experts for validation. The trouble was that much of the material did not appear to have come from the Himalayas, but from other areas, particularly Bohemia, where the Professor had been.

A co-author of a paper on trilobites, Fred Shaw from Lehman College in the Bronx, was sufficiently intrigued to make a journey to Chandrigar only to find the Professor was 'unavailable'. A subsequent paper in *Nature* by the Australian academic John Talent discredited the work of Professor Gupta.

The problem with scientific fraud is that the complainer – 'whistle blower' – often comes out of the conflict with his or her reputation damaged far more than that of the fraudster. The solution to this is to establish an independent body to investigate such claims. In the US the Office of Research Integrity considers the evidence both with legal and scientific bases (but see Case 6 above). It has had to consider over 200 cases in a two-year period. In Denmark the Commission of Scientific Dishonesty has had to consider 21 cases in two years. Both Finland and Norway have similar bodies. No such commission exists in the UK as yet (2003). Too often cases of alleged misconduct arise from personal vendettas and it is vital that they are considered and evaluated by neutral adjudicators. Recently retired assessors would be ideal, since they have no vested interest in the outcome.

CHAPTER TEN

SCIENCE, RELIGION AND MIND

Consciousness, being abstract, is hard to define. It is the basic non-physical element. Evidence of it is shown in the response to stimuli, which may be either active or passive. It probably evolved, like everything else, as a response to the need of a primitive organism for food or a mate. At any rate, it appears to be the result of neuronal activity (there are estimated 10^9 neurones in a human brain). An essential feature of consciousness is memory. This again is a consequence of neuronal activity, and may well be similar in nature to the memory of a calculator or computer. Synapses (the connections of nerve fibres in the brain) have features in common with the semiconductor junction, one of which is that they will allow the passage of an electric current one way but not the other.

There are several Altered States of Consciousness, with different causation. The first two are physiological, the remainder, pathological.

1. Sleep. It is necessary to delete all the unwanted memories, particularly visual, that have accumulated during wakefulness, whether conscious or unconscious. The dolphin, an air breathing mammal, needs to surface from time to time. Apparently only half of its brain sleeps at a time. If it were not for this, it would drown.
2. Sexual arousal. This occurs during appropriate circumstances. It also occurs during paradoxical (REM – rapid eye movement) sleep.
3. Toxic delirium, such as high fever.
4. Hypnosis. This is a consequence of the learning process, or one might say, an exploitation of the learning process, used by demagogues. Religious and military exaltation

may be a manifestation of mass hypnosis. Auto-hypnosis is also possible.

5. Drugs. Response to psychoactive drugs is unpredictable, may be lethal. Usually they make people happy but goofy. A 'trip' was eloquently described by Henry James as 'a mood of vertiginous amazement at a meaningless infinity'. Perhaps 'goofy' is better.

6. Epilepsy.

7. Hysteria (dissociation). Uncommon today in developed countries.

8. Head injury. Confusion leading to coma.

9. Brain disease, such as tumour or Alzheimer's disease.

Language is programmed into the infant by his or her mother (this is similar to the 'booting' of a computer). It is stored in the brain – the passive mind (named thus by Aristotle – also called the subconscious by Sigmund Freud). The computer analogue of the passive mind is the hard disc. It is accessed by the active mind, the conscious. The conscious mind is the analogue of the central processing unit, with its random access memory (consciousness is the interface between the physical and the non-physical elements of the brain). RAM is the computer analogue of the intellectual cognitive (speech, literacy and numeracy) component of the mind. The ROM (Read Only Memory) is the analogue of the instinctive component. In between these lies the emotions.

Both the active and passive minds constitute the non-physical element of the personality. Just as some computers have more RAM than others, so some people's minds work faster than others. Consequent to this idea, the crashing of a computer has certain similarities to the nervous breakdown of *Homo sapiens*.

When a computer is presented with a task it cannot fulfil given its inadequate speed or memory or just that the task is impossible, it may crash, that is to say, it will not accept any input nor will it produce any output. The only thing to do is to switch it off and start again, or press the reset button if there is one. Likewise a person presented with an impossible situation, given his or her intellectual or emotional state, may cease to respond sensibly. The thing to do then is to switch off the brain by means of rest, TLC and appropriate medication until normal service is resumed. The French physician Phillipe **Pinel** in 1792 released the shackles from the inmates of the Salpetrière in Paris, in the belief that there was nobody whose behaviour could not be improved by being treated with kindness rather than cruelty.

Learning appears to work mainly in a positive sense. One can persuade people to do things and believe things but it is difficult to persuade people not to do things. That is why anti-sex and anti-drug education and legislation are singularly unsuccessful.

In his long history of evolution, Man has developed language, in order to facilitate communication. Then came abstract thought, then came ideas, with the notion of God, then came writing. Then the conscience developed. This is epitomised in the *Golden Rule* – the perennial philosophy, common to all philosophies and religions – Do Unto Others as you Would that They Should do unto You. In the unfortunate condition of psychopathy sufferers appear not to have developed a conscience.

A *totem* is an animal or the spirit of an animal which gives the clan its name and with which it shares allegiance and mutual protection, and upon which the tribe may be dependent. The animal is respected, not always killed and eaten. In Hinduism, the spirits of the dead are believed to inhabit the bodies of monkeys, which are held sacred. Similar beliefs are found in Australian Aboriginal culture. Perhaps the totem of the early Judaeo/Christian religion was the sheep (Agnus Dei).

Animism is a primitive religion one feature of which is an altered state of consciousness induced by physical means, such as repeated mantras, drugs, whirling etc. It is the basis of *astrology*. Early Man, gazing at the stars, identified patterns which were supposed to correspond to various animals. The character of the animal is in some way supposed to represent the character of the individual born under the particular constellation, and his or her future can be foretold by reference to his or her birth time and date. There has never been any evidence for the truth of this, yet many eminent individuals consult astrologers.

Perhaps it is a way of transferring or avoiding responsibility for one's action.

Living creatures have three elements to be considered. Body (physical), Mind (non-physical) and Spirit. The Chinese have the word Qi or Chi, the Japanese the word Reiki, variously translated as 'life force' or nervous or emotional energy, or even perhaps 'motivation'. There is no equivalent word in the English language, which makes discussion difficult. At any rate the principal underlying factor appears to be group activity. A group can accomplish more than the sum total of individual effort. Religion is a powerful motivating force. Love is a great stimulus to activity as, regrettably, is hate, especially jealousy

Some people, the 'charismatic' have the ability to stimulate and control activity, the leaders of the world, for better or worse. They are at the top of the dominance hierarchy tree. Others have the ability to access people's passive memory or subconscious mind. They are the psychics or mediums, who sometimes claim to communicate with the dead – necromancy.

Unfortunately this can lead to an emotional transference situation and dependency, with loss of autonomy and money. Drugs, both legal and illegal, are increasingly used to stimulate nervous energy. Since the physiological balance is upset, increasing doses may be required to obtain the desired effect leading to dependency and addiction, with a corresponding loss of rational thought and social isolation, which is a significant factor in suicide.

The word 'Religion' is derived from the Latin *religio* – 'I bind'. Therefore a religion is a group of people bound by a set of values or beliefs. Man, by virtue of his nature as a social animal, tends to live in groups, and develop a dominance hierarchy system (similar to the 'peck order' of chickens) and from such groups leaders become identified, to whom the members defer, and owe loyalty and allegiance. The leader seeks to justify his position by asserting that his authority derives from God – Divine Right.

Different ethnic groups have of course different names for this concept. The ancient Egyptians had the Sun God Ra, (complete with halo), the Greeks had Zeus, the Romans, Jupiter, the Hebrews Jehovah, the Muslims Allah, and so on. There was always a close relation between the leader (king) and his high priest (shaman, who had direct communication with God). The king chose the high priest, and the priest crowns the king, thereby giving him legitimacy. It became necessary to separate the various administrative functions, and specialisation occurred, and gods of war, fertility, agriculture, love, wine etc., were postulated, together with their priests and priestesses, all of whom enjoyed prestige and privilege. Today we have various Governmental Ministries and Departments.

In the Hindu dominance hierarchy or caste system as it is known, the Priest or Brahmin is the highest, then comes the soldier, then the farmer, then the clerk, then the cleaner (untouchable). Justification for this established order of things and social position calls for faith – belief, not evidence. The origin of these systems of belief is not clear. They may well have evolved in order to justify territorial expansion 'God is on our side' – 'It is God's will', or merely to justify the status quo. The notion of survival after death is clearly of advantage to the military; fear of death and its avoidance is the fundamental fear of all living creatures.

Since religion is based on faith, and science is based on reason and evidence, there is inevitably a logical and intellectual conflict. In fact the two are irreconcilable. It may well be that the two are necessary for emotional and rational development and evolution. One can no more deny the world of emotion or feeling or instinct than one can deny the world of reason. The two are complementary and necessary.

A *theocracy* can be considered as a combination of State and religious power whose function is to keep the community together, to prevent its destruction by perceived outside interference, just as an organism seeks to preserve its identity and autonomy by developing immune reactions against microbes. This is the basis of *paranoia*, when perceived dangers become irrational and mental balance is disturbed. Sometimes the physiological immune response itself becomes destructive, when the body starts manufacturing antibodies against itself, with the development of auto-immune diseases.

Perhaps the last theocracy is in Buddhist Tibet, with its God/King, the Dalai Lama. It struggles to survive as an independent entity, in the face of relentless progress, as its principle of non-violence renders it vulnerable to external force.

Many people find scientific determinism unacceptable. People like to think that they do have some higher purpose in life, that their activities and thoughts do have consequences, that there is more to life than mere survival and reproduction, that all is not predetermined

Then there is the concept of *free will*. This is best explained by analogy. A billiard ball does not have freewill. Its movements are entirely a consequence of past events. A sentient being, on the other hand has alternatives – he or she can go to the right or the left depending not only on past events but on future desires, intentions or consequences. An inanimate object has no such choice. If one defines intelligence as the ability to process information, a beetle is as intelligent as a computer, except that a beetle, unlike a computer, has free will in that he can go to the right or the left in pursuit of that which will confer advantage to it.

Consider the question 'why is the Earth round?' A theology student might answer 'God made the Earth round so that we should not see too far what lay ahead'. A science student might answer 'The spherical configuration of the globe exists on account of the operation of the second law of thermodynamics, in that this shape maximizes its entropy. Both answers might be considered correct, though quite incomprehensible to the opposite discipline.

Science deals with the objective, religion with the subjective. Both are necessary, and complementary.

The French philosopher and mathematician Rene Descartes (1596-1650) is known for his saying *'cogito ergo sum'* – I think therefore I am. It might well be more appropriate to say *'credo ergo sum'* – I believe therefore I am. Integrity of the personality depends on a system of belief. One can consider the brain as a computer which is programmed from birth, firstly with language then with belief, though the two are inextricably inter-woven. 'Give me a child until he is seven and he is mine for life' claims the Jesuit. It is no coincidence that the brain continues to grow until the age of seven. A brain-injured child under the age of seven can grow up with no detectable deficit. After that age there may well be some impairment.

In order to understand the nature of belief one can start by considering the placebo effect. A *placebo* (Latin: I will please) is an effect or intention rather than a tablet or medication. It oper-ates equally whether the medication is pharmacologically active or pharmacologically inactive, and depends on the attitude of the practitioner. It is particularly effective in non-physical con-ditions such as headaches, to the extent that 30% of people will experience relief from a 'dummy' tablet devoid of pharmacolog-ical activity. Some people respond better then others – they could be called 'placebo responders' or perhaps 'suggestible'. The more powerful the suggestion, the more effective the response. Witch doctors, ngangas, are expert at this and can even persuade people to death. Likewise, they can also be cred-ited with magical cures. Objective belief requires evidence. Subjective belief does not – merely powerful suggestion. Those who seek evidence for the existence of God are doomed to dis-appointment, since the notion of God is abstract, not objective but subjective, no less real for some, or necessary.

Many of the most sublime manifestations of music, art and architecture have been based on religious dedication – To the Glory of God, even though the composers, artists, architects and masons concerned may not have been particularly pious. It is interesting to speculate that stone circles, the most splendid of which is Stonehenge, perhaps represents Man's early need to delineate a piece of territory, which, having been consecrated, is devoted to the performance of symbolic rituals associated with the chiefs and dominant families of the tribe, who claim leader-ship and possession of the territory. Also with the performance of rituals associated with those three elements of family life – birth, marriage and death; significant events in effecting the cohesion of the family and loyalty of the tribe.

Perhaps Westminster Abbey would be the modern equivalent.

Westminster Abbey is but 1000 years old, whereas Stonehenge is 3,800 years old.

And yet it is hard to believe that evolution has occurred purely as a result of random activity, that all that has been or will be is purely chance. Statistically, it seems unlikely; and that there is an underlying purpose driving it all, whatever that may be. 'Once', said Winston Churchill after a particularly good dinner, 'I thought I understood the meaning and purpose of life. Unfortunately, by the following morning, I had forgotten what it was.'

Religion, like everything else, has evolved as a response to need. Behavioural change, from primitive to more complex and elaborate practices and beliefs, is based on the obligatory primate instincts, the necessity to belong, to create, to communicate and to explore. Particularly, to answer questions such as 'where have we come from?' and 'where are we going?'

And religion provides an answer to the questions that science cannot. Fear of death and its aftermath is fundamental. 'Losing God changed my whole outlook – it left fear as the dominant emotion' (Wendy Perriam). Therefore religion is about belonging and about death. There is nothing like a funeral to remind people of God. 'Ashes to Ashes, Dust to Dust' as the mortal (physical) remains are committed to Earth or Fire. But the Soul (non-physical) goes Marching On.

We, like all living creatures, have been allotted by Divine Providence, or perhaps Inscrutable Fate, depending on one's belief, a certain amount of time and a certain amount of space. We must use it creatively (good) rather then destructively (bad).

A sensible philosophy of life is to look forward, not backward. What is done is done and cannot be undone.

The moving finger writes and having writ, moves on.
Nor all they piety nor wit can call it back to alter half a line.
Nor all thy tears wash out a word of it.

Omar Khayyam.

EPILOGUE

No man is an island, entire of itself;
Every man is a piece of the continent, a part of the main;
If a clod be washed away by the sea, Europe is the less.
Any man's death diminishes me because I am involved
in Mankind;
And therefore never send to know for whom the bell tolls;
It tolls for thee.

> *Meditation XVII*
> John Donne (1571–1631)

With Earth's first clay they did the last man knead,
And there of the last harvest sowed the seed.
The first morning of creation wrote
What the last dawn of reckoning shall read.

> *Rubaiyat of Omar Khayyam*
> Twelfth century Persia

Man, proud Man,
Drest in a little brief authority,
Most ignorant of what he's most assured,
His glassy essence, Like an angry Ape,
Plays such fantastic tricks before high heaven
As make the Angels weep.

> *Measure for Measure.*
> William Shakespeare (1564-1616)

Sole judge of truth, in endless error hurl'd
The Glory, Jest, and Riddle of the World.

> *Essay on Man.*
> Alexander Pope, (1688–1744)

A BRIEF HISTORY OF SCIENCE

Tu Modo, dum lucet, fructum ne desere vitae.
(Only therefore, while the light remains, let us
not forsake the joy of life.)

Elegies.
Sextus Propertius (50–15BC)

THE HUMAN BEING AND THE DINOSAUR.
(from *Further Fables of Our Time* by James Thurber)

Ages ago, in a wasteland of time and a wilderness of space, Man, in upper case, and dinosaur, in lower, first came face to face. They stood like stones for a long while, wary and watchful, taking each other in. Something told the dinosaur that he beheld before him the coming glory and terror of the world, and in the still air of the young planet he seemed to catch the faint smell of his own inevitable doom.

'Greetings, stupid,' said Man. 'Behold in me the artfully articulated architect of the future, the chosen species, the certain survivor, the indestructible one, the monarch of all you survey, and all that everyone else surveys, for that matter. On the other hand, you are, for all your size, a member of the inconsequent ephemera. You are one of God's moderately amusing early experiments, a frail footnote to natural history, a contraption in a museum for future Man to marvel at, an excellent example of Jehovah's jejune juvenilia.'

The dinosaur sighed with a sound like thunder.

'Perpetuating your species', Man continued, 'would be foolish and futile.'

'The missing link is not lost,' said the dinosaur sorrowfully. 'It's hiding.'

Man paid the doomed dinosaur no mind.

'If there were no Man it would be necessary to create one,' said the Man, 'for God moves in mysterious, but inefficient ways, and He needs help. Man will go on for ever but you will be one with the mammoth and the mastodon, for monstrosity is the behemother of extinction.'

'There are worse things than being extinct' said the dinosaur sourly, 'and one of them is being you.'

Man strutted a little pace and flexed his muscles. 'You cannot commit murder' he said, 'for murder requires a mind. You are only capable of dinosaurslaughter. You and your ilk are incapable of devising increasingly effective methods of destroying your own species, and at the same time increasingly miraculous methods of keeping it extant. You will never live to know the two-party system, the multi-party system, and the one-party system. You will have gone long before I have made this the best of all possible worlds, no matter how possible all other worlds may be.

'In your highest state of evolution you could not develop the brain cells to prove innocent men guilty, even after their acquittal. You are all wrong in the crotch, and in the cranium, and in the cortex. But I have wasted enough time on you. I must use these fingers which God gave me, and now wishes He has kept for himself, to begin writing those noble volumes about Me, which will one day run to several hundred billion items, many of them about war, death, conquest, decline, fall, blood, sweat, tears, threats, warnings, boasts, hopelessness, hell, heels, and whores. There will be little enough about you and your ilk and your kith and your kin, for, after all, who were you and your ilk and your kith and your kin?'

'Good day and good-bye,' said the Man in conclusion. 'I shall see to it that your species receives a decent burial, with some simple ceremony.'

Man, as it turned out, was right. The dinosaur and his ilk and his kith and his kin died not long after, still in lower case, but with a curious smile of satisfaction, or something of the sort, on their ephemeral faces.

MORAL: The noblest study of mankind is Man, says Man.

BIBLIOGRAPHY

1. Asimov's *New Guide to Science*. Penguin 1987
2. Final Report of Metrication Board. HMSO.
3. *Too Hot to Handle*. Frank Close, 1990. W.H.Allen.
4. *Dictionary of Scientific Units*. Jerrard & McNeill 1992. Chapman & Hall.
5. *The Case of the Midwife Toad*. Arthur Koestler. 1971 Hutchinson & Co.
6. *Fraud and Misconduct in Medical Research*. Lock & Wells. 1993. BMJ Publishing Group.
7. *Nobel – The Man and his Prizes* - Nobel Foundation and W. Odelburg. Elsevier 1962.
8. *Piltdown*. Frank Spencer. OUP
9. *The Major Achievements of Science* - McKenzie. Camb.U.P.
10. *The Fontana History of Chemistry* - Brock. Fontana. 1992.
11. *Famous Chemists* - Tilden. Routledge. 1921.
12. *Age of the Earth*. John Thackray. HMSO. 1980.
13. *Age of the Earth*. Arthur Holmes. Thomas Nelson. 1937.
14. *Benjamin Thompson, Count Rumford*. S.C.Brown. MIT Press.
15. *The Baltimore Case*. Daniel J. Kevles. W.W.Norton, & Co. Ltd. 1998.
16. *Sir Cyril Burt*. L.S.Hearnshaw. Hodder & Stoughton, 1979.
17. *The Dinosaur Hunters*. Deborah Cadbury. Fourth Estate, London. 2000.
18. *Isaac Newton – the Last Sorcerer*. Michael White. Fourth Estate.1997
19. *Fly-An Experimental Life*- Martin Brooks. Weidenfeld and Nicholson. 2001.
20. *A Monk and Two Peas*. Robin Marantz Henig. Weidenfeld and Nicholson.2000.
21. *Crippen, the Mild Murderer*. Tom Cullen. The Bodley Head, 1977.
22. *Science Book*. Cassell & Co. 2001.
23. *The Compleat Naturalist - a Life of Linnaeus*. W.Blunt. Francis Lincoln Ltd,2001.
24. *The Map that Changed the World*. Simon Winchester. Viking, 2001. Penguin,2002.

25. *A Beautiful Mind.* Sylvia Nasar. Faber & Faber. 2001
26. *The Worst Accident in the World.* Hawkes, et al. Pan and Heinemann 1986.
27. *Science – A History.* John Gribben Allen Lane 2002.
28. *Encyclopaedia Britannica,* 14th edition, 1929.

APPENDIX 1

LIST OF PREFIXES

Prefix	Abbreviation	Power of Ten	Value
TERA	T	10^{12}	Million million (trillion)
GIGA	G	10^{9}	Thousand million (billion)
MEGA	M	10^{6}	Million
KILO	K	10^{3}	Thousand
HECTO	H	10^{2}	Hundred
DECA	dk	10^{1}	Ten
		10^{0}	Unit
DECI	d	10^{-1}	Tenths
CENT1	c	10^{-2}	Hundredths
MILLI	m	10^{-3}	Thousandths
MICRO	µ	10^{-6}	Millionths

(The symbol µ is also used to indicate
a millionth part of a metre)

NANO	n	10^{-9}	Thousand millionths
PICO	p	10^{-12}	Million millionths
FEMTO	f	10^{-15}	
ATTO	a	10^{-18}	

Approximate examples

Streptococcus	$1µ$ (10^{-6} metres)
Virus	$0.1µ = 100$ nanometres
Molecule	1 nanometre (nm)
Atom	0.1nm $= 100$ picometres
Nucleus (of atom)	10 femtometres
Proton	1 femtometre
Quark	1 attometre.

APPENDIX 2

SOME FREEZING AND BOILING POINTS

The symbol K means degrees Kelvin which is absolute zero, -273.16°C

SUBSTANCE	FREEZING OR MELTING POINT	BOILING POINT	
Helium	>1K (at 25 Bar)	-268.9°C	4.2K (at 1 Bar)
Hydrogen	14K (-259°C)	-240°C	33K
Nitrogen	-209°C	-195°C	78K
Oxygen	-218°C:	-183°C	90K
Carbon Dioxide	31°C	-78.5°C	194.7K
Chlorine	-101°C	33.97°C	238.7K
Ethyl Alcohol	-112°C	78°C	
Water	0°C	100°C	
Mercury	-39°C	357°C	
Iron	1535°C	2480°C	

APPENDIX 3

RADIOACTIVITY

When the radioactive isotope of an element disintegrates, the time for half of the element to remain is known as the half-life. It is characteristic of the isotope.

Three types of emission occur.

1. <u>Alpha particles</u> are slow moving helium nuclei, with a positive charge. They can be stopped by a layer of paper.

2. <u>Beta particles</u> are electrons and move more rapidly and are more penetrating.
Beta decay involves emission of an electron from a proton, which becomes a neutron. They will penetrate about 1cm of skin.

3. <u>Gamma rays</u> are high energy photons, very penetrating, can penetrate steel, blocked by lead, and can be detected by their property of causing a gas to ionise, by removing an electron from the outer shell of the atom. When this happens the gas will conduct an electric current, which can be detected. This is the basis of the Geiger-Muller Counter. Gamma rays from each element have a characteristic energy, wavelength and frequency. $E = h\nu$. $\lambda = c/\nu$, where h is Planck's constant ν is the frequency, λ is the wavelength and c is the velocity of light. Gamma rays cause great damage to all living tissues, the greater the 'dose' (intensity times time) the greater the damage. Gamma rays can also be detected by their property of causing fogging of a photographic plate, similar to photons of light, by virtue of their ability to 'reduce' silver ions.

APPENDIX 4

HALF LIVES OF SOME COMMON ISOTOPES
(The atomic mass is indicated by a superscript)

Isotopes marked with an * decay when a proton disintegrates into a neutron and a positron. The positron (anti-matter) rapidly captures an electron, which are in abundance, and both are annihilated with the release of a photon of gamma rays which can then be detected by instruments such as a Scintillation Counter. This phenomenon is used medically in Positron Emission Tomography. Since these isotopes have such short half-lives, they have to be prepared locally in a cyclotron.

Isotope	Half life
^{3}H (Tritium)	12 years β-decay
^{11}Carbon*	20 minutes*
^{14}Carbon	5,570 years
^{13}Nitrogen	10 minutes*
^{15}Oxygen	2 minutes*
^{40}Potassium	1,300 million years
^{41}Argon	1.8 hours
^{85}Krypton	10.8 years
^{87}Rubidium	47,000 million years
^{60}Cobalt	5.7 years intense γ emitter
^{90}Strontium	29 years α emitter† (see below)
^{99}Technetium	211,100 years
^{129}Iodine	10 million years
^{131}Iodine	8 days
^{137}Caesium	30 years α emitter† (see below)
^{210}Polonium	138 days α emitter
^{222}Radon (Gas)	3.8 days α emitter, becomes polonium
^{236}Radium	1620 years α emitter, becomes radon
^{232}Thorium	13,900 million years
^{237}Neptunium	2.14 million years
^{235}Uranium	713 million years
^{238}Uranium	4,510 million years
^{239}Plutonium	24,110 years
^{243}Americium	432.2 years

†At 1.23am on Friday, April 5 1986, a fireball exploded in the night sky over the roof of reactor No 4 (1000 MW RMBK type) at the *Chernobyl* Nuclear Power Station, supplying Kiev, the capital city of the Ukraine. The reactor had exploded, leaving a gaping hole in its top. A plume of hot, intensely radioactive debris rose into the atmosphere to a height of 3000 feet. From there it spread out to most of Europe, causing *fallout* of radio-active elements, particularly in rainfall. The most dangerous are caesium, strontium and iodine. Caesium is a Group 1A alkali metal similar to potassium and the body cannot distinguish them. It is therefore absorbed and incorporated into all living tissue. Similarly the body cannot distinguish between strontium and calcium and Sr^{90} is absorbed and incorporated particularly into the bone marrow, where it damages the blood-forming tissue leading to leukaemia and aplastic anaemia. Iodine is taken up by the thyroid gland and radioactive iodine causes a greatly increased incidence of cancer of the thyroid, particularly in children.

APPENDIX 5

(Designated SI in all languages)

This has been adopted since the mid 1970s as the legal units for trade in over 30 countries, and for use by scientists. There are 7 base units and 22 derived units.

The 7 base units are as follows:

1. MASS – the **kilogram** is based on the prototype cylinder at Sèvres.

2. LENGTH – the **metre** is defined as 1,650,763.73 wavelengths in vacuo of radiation corresponding to the transition between levels 2p10 and 5d5 of the krypton 86 atom,

3. TIME – the **second** is defined as above using the period of the Caesium 133 atom.

4. Temperature – The **Kelvin** is the fraction 1/273.16 of the thermodynamic temperature of the triple point of water (freezing point). 1 degree Celsius = I K.

5. The **Candela** is the Unit of Luminance.

6. The **Ampère** is the unit of electric current.

7. The **Mole** is the unit of quantity of matter. It is the amount of a substance in grams equal to its molecular weight expressed in atomic mass units.

The derived units include:

1. Pressure – This is the force acting at right angles to a unit area
1 **Pascal** is defined as 1 Newton per square metre.
1 **Bar** is 10^5 Pascals, 14.5 pounds per square inch or 1

million dynes per square centimetre.

Old units are:

1. 1 Atmosphere = 760mm of mercury = 98,066.5 Pa =14.7 pounds per square inch at sea level.

2. 1mm of mercury = 133,322 Pa = 13.595 inches of water. Historically, and for convenience, blood pressure is measured in millimetres of mercury, Domestic Gas pressure in inches of water, car tyre pressure in pounds per square inch or Bar, Atmospheric pressure in millibars. (An obsolete unit of pressure is the *torr*, equal to 1 millimetre of mercury – still in use in the US.

2. The unit of force is the **Newton**. It is the force required to accelerate 1 kilogram by 1 metre per second per second and is equal to 10^5 dynes. Force has magnitude and direction.

3 The *Joule* is the unit of work done. It is equal to a force of one Newton acting over a distance of one metre, and is equivalent to 10^7 ergs or a watt–second.

4. The *Calorie* is a unit of heat representing the quarter of heat required to raise the temperature of one gram of water through one degree Celsius. Unfortunately it varies with the temperature of the water and has been superseded by the joule, and is equal to 4.184 joules.

SUBJECT INDEX

INDEX OF NAMES